discoveries

COLLEGE LIBRARY

Please return this book by the date stamped below
- if recalled, the loan is reduced to 10 days

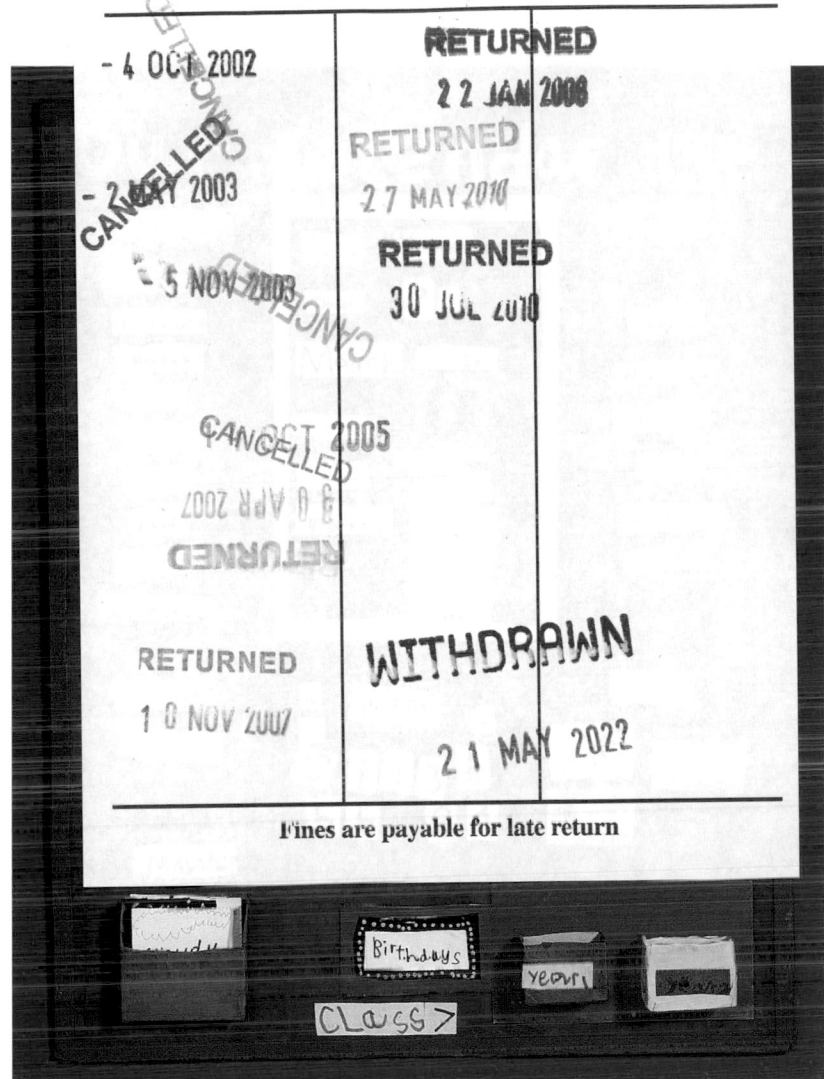

Fines are payable for late return

Katherine Cuthbert

Acknowledgements

The author and publishers would like to thank the teachers and children from the following schools for their co-operation, contributions and support during the preparation of this book:
Sudbourne Primary School, especially the Headteacher, Susan Scarsbrook, for her invaluable encouragement and enthusiasm.
Reay Primary School, especially the Headteacher, Peter Charan.
Alleyns Junior School, especially the Headteacher, Bridget Weir, and also Rachel Barnes.

They would also like to thank Colin Uttley of the Science Museum, London, for his help and advice on the Bread project, Graham Dolan of the Old Royal Observatory, Greenwich, for his help with the 'All in Good Time' project, Patrick McKee, Paul Newham and Peter Roud of the South London Science and Technology Centre, for all their help and advice.

The author and publishers would like to give special thanks to Edmund Cuthbert for all his ideas and contributions, especially the models shown on the front cover and below.

Line drawings by Katherine Cuthbert

First Published in 1998 by
BELAIR PUBLICATIONS LIMITED
Albert House, Apex Business Centre, Boscombe Road, Dunstable, Beds LU5 4RL
© 1998 Katherine Cuthbert
Editor Robyn Gordon
Designed by Lynn Hooker
Photography by Kelvin Freeman and Mark Limberg
ISBN 0 947882 79 0
Printed in Hong Kong through World Print

Contents

INTRODUCTION

This book combines the exciting worlds of science, design and language, and presents many opportunities for children to explore, investigate and discuss scientific concepts and then use their discoveries as a springboard for designing and making their own unique creations. Not only will this offer the children a real challenge, but allows them to create something tangible that they can relate to their learning.

Reading, writing and researching are among the many skills embedded within each project and, presented in an interesting way, are guaranteed to promote enthusiasm and co-operative teamwork, as children transform their ideas into reality.

DISPLAY

Children are encouraged to plan and create their own displays as part of each project. This allows them to record and celebrate what they have learned, and makes them feel much more involved in the whole learning process. In creating their own displays, children actually extend their design skills: they have to plan, co-operate and make decisions. They can make their displays into resource boards, by making them interactive or even making them into guessing games, challenges or quizzes.

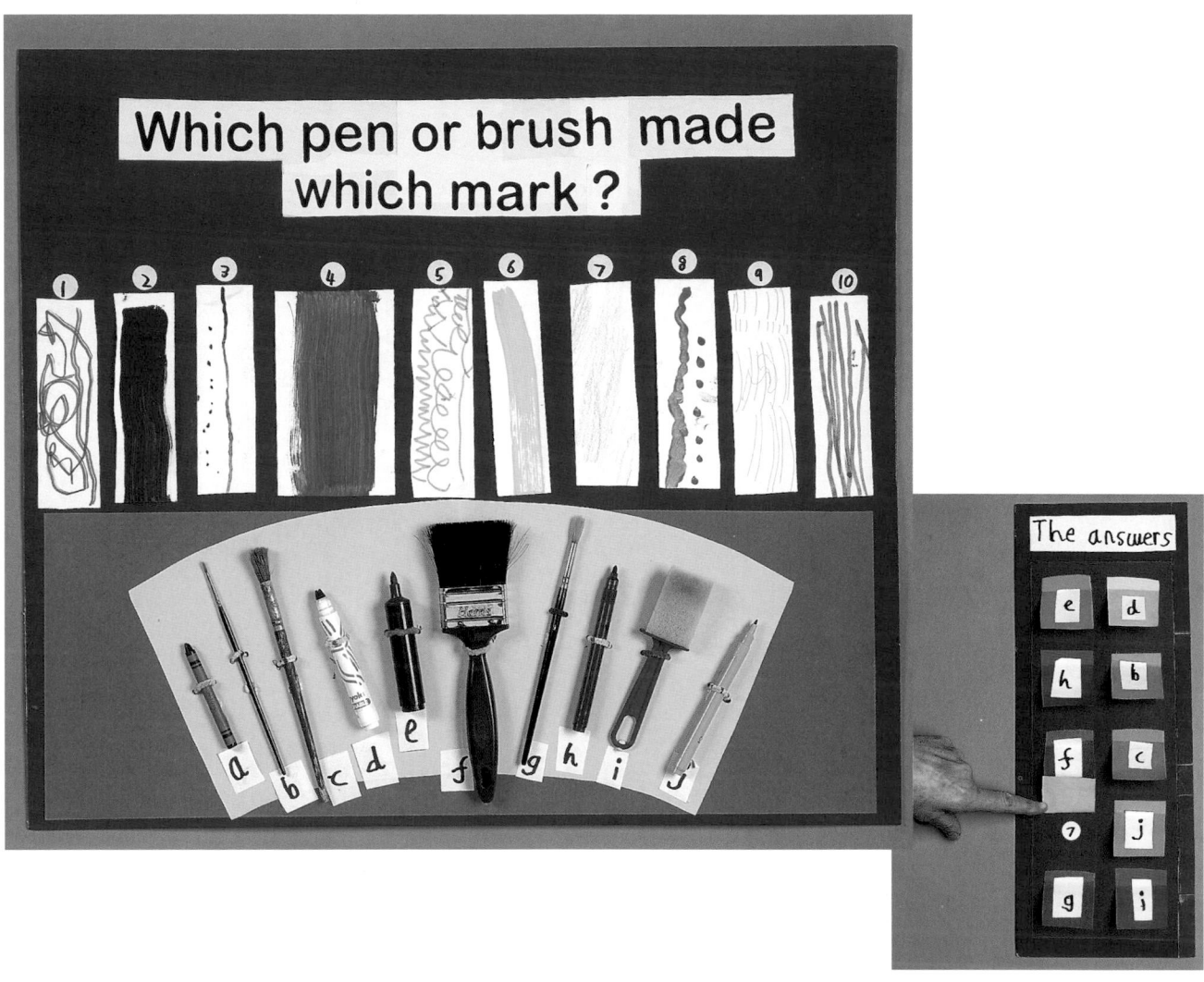

Such displays can become a resource for the whole school, and the children have the satisfaction of seeing their explorations, experiments and discoveries become something that the whole school can share in and learn from. When designing their display boards, the children should always be encouraged to consider their intended audience and ask questions like: "Are the labels clear? Is the layout easy to understand?" They should stand back from the display as it progresses, to view it from a distance. Making displays together provides many opportunities for discussion and communication. Equally, showing another class their work can be very valuable and enables the teacher to assess what the children have learned.

LETTERING

The word processor is a useful tool for children to create a whole range of unusual and interesting lettering. Children should have opportunities to explore the different styles, size and colour of fonts for use in labelling their diagrams and displays. Here are some ideas for other styles of lettering:

Newsprint, cut out and enlarged on the photocopier

Sponge letters, dipped into plaster of Paris and then painted

Writing on two layers of paper, with bottom layer slid to one side to give a shadow effect

Three-dimensional lettering - in this case using zig-zag folded paper to create a 'springs' effect

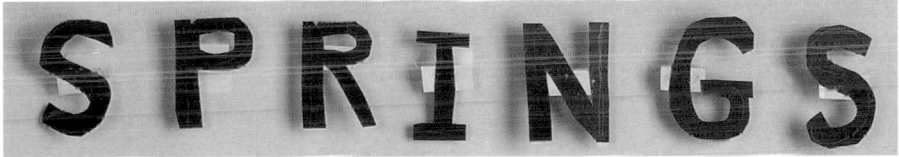

Decorated bubble writing

Decorated letters

TECHNIQUES

Joining boxes

To join boxes, use PVA glue and just enough masking tape to hold the join together. Then use either gummed tape (using a bowl of water or a wet sponge to moisten the gummed tape) or thinned-down PVA and strips of newspaper to cover the join well. Once dried overnight, this will be a very strong join. (The Hickory, Dickory, Dock clocks were made using this technique to join several boxes together.)

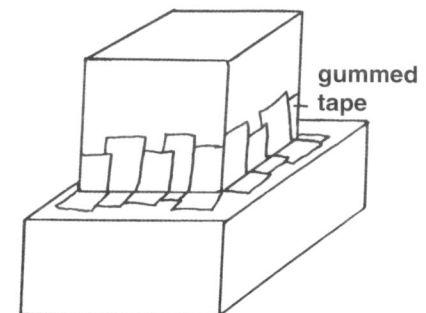

gummed tape

Round or oval shapes

For round or oval shapes, squash newspaper into a ball and tape together with masking tape to hold the shape. Cover with one layer of newspaper strips or tissue paper, liberally painted with thinned-down PVA glue. (The heads in the electricity project were made this way.)

Another method is to blow up a balloon and cover it in three or four layers of gummed tape. This makes a very strong shell structure. (Humpty Dumpty was made using this technique.)

Gluing tubes

To glue tubes, cut around the top and bend over to give a larger gluing surface, then use a lot of PVA and hold in place with masking tape. Cover the join with thinned-down PVA and newspaper strips and leave to dry overnight.

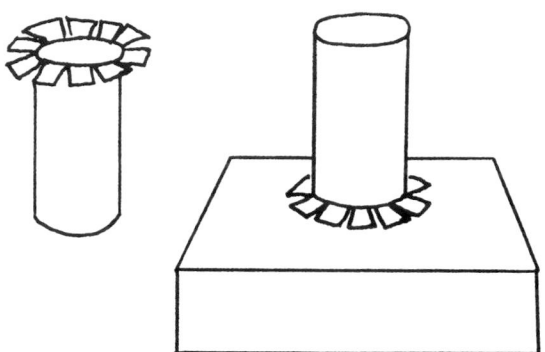

Clay

Make sure that the clay is soft and malleable. Hard clay is impossible to model or join properly. When joining clay, the children must use 'clay glue' (or slip). Without it their models will fall apart when dry.

Show the children how to roll a small ball of clay in their hands and then use their thumb to push a hole into the middle of the ball. They should then squeeze the clay between their thumb and fingers, whilst turning the ball around in their hand to make a little pot (this is called a pinch pot). They can then put a bit of water in their pot and stir it around with a stiff paintbrush until some of the clay combines with the water. This is called 'slip', and it acts as a glue to stick clay together.

Joining woodstrip

Joining woodstrip can be difficult, as it is not easy for the children to make an accurate mitre cut which is needed for the end grains to bond together. It is much easier for children to simply cut the wood straight across, which means that they are then joining the end grain to the straight grain. This join would have very little strength without the use of a triangular card corner (where the strength of the join comes from the fact that the two lengths of wood are joined by the card). The join can be held in a jig, or with masking tape, bulldog clips or G clamps, while the glue dries overnight.

Note: A way of storing reclaimed boxes is to undo them at the glue joins, flatten them, and then make them up again with glue when needed. When putting the boxes together again, they can be glued inside-out so that the outside is plain. (Children can learn a lot about the nets of boxes from this activity.)

TOOLS AND SAFETY

The safe use of tools and materials must be given the highest priority. It is important that, from the start, children are taught to work with tools and equipment both safely and correctly and are aware of the potential hazards.

Do not allow children to wander around the classroom with sharp tools. It is best when working with tools that one table is allocated for tool use only. Children can then go to that table when they need to use a tool, and return to their own table to continue work that does not need the tools.

It is important for the children to have a sense of order in their working environment. Clearly labelled and organized resources help the children choose tools and equipment for themselves. They should learn to be tidy, put things back where they came from, clean up after themselves, and to respect other people's work. To this end, it is most important to provide adequate workspace.

It is a good idea to encourage the children to observe and draw the tools they use, as they then examine them more carefully and accurately. (All illustrations in this book which have been done by children have a blue border.)

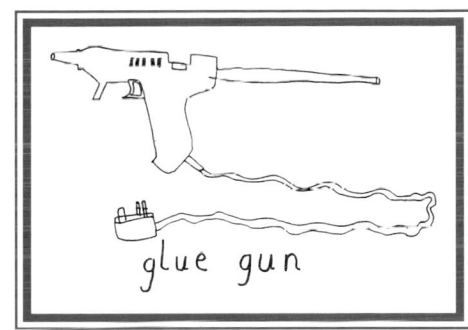

glue gun

THE TOOLS

The tools most frequently used for the projects in this book are common to most primary schools and classrooms.

Safety goggles
Always ask the children to wear safety goggles if there is any possibility of danger from tools or materials.

Junior hacksaws
These are lightweight and quite easy for children to handle. Do make sure that they are held correctly, with the forefinger along the length of the hacksaw and with the other three fingers and thumb grasping the handle. The forefinger stops the hacksaw from wobbling from side to side. When sawing, do not press down on to the blade, as the blades bend under pressure. The blades also clog up easily, so check them periodically. When changing the blades, make sure that the teeth face away from the handle. Explain to the children that the blades only cut in a forwards direction. If the blades stick while sawing, pull lightly over a piece of wax (for example, a candle).

Scissors
Scissors are used for cutting paper, card and fabric. Use the whole length of the blade, not just the tips. Check periodically to make sure that they are not blunt.

Hammers
Use a light pin hammer or a small claw hammer. Check periodically that the heads are firmly fixed into the shaft. Balance the hammer by holding the end of the handle. Hold firmly. Gravity will help the fall.

Hole punch

Either two hole or single hole punches are very useful tools for making neat holes. They can, however, only make holes along the edge of materials.

Paper drill

This very useful tool will make holes anywhere. They come with hole bits of different sizes.

Bench vice

Children should be taught to hold their dowel and woodstrip in a vice to cut it, as this kind of material can spring back very easily, and is safer when held fast. The jaws of a vice are very strong: do explain the dangers to the children.

Pliers

Pliers are tools for cutting and holding. The jaws have a serrated edge allowing for a firm grip. They also have a short blade which can cut through hard materials like wire. These should be used only with adult supervision and children should be taught to keep fingers well away from the jaws of the pliers.

GLUES

PVA

This is a very useful glue and can be used as it is, or thinned down with water. It is best spread with a stiff brush - keep special brushes for this, as it is very strong once dry. Show the children how to wash the brushes out thoroughly after use. Avoid eye contact, as it can be an irritant.

Glue sticks

A very good glue for sticking paper together, especially where things need to be kept dry.

All-purpose solvent-free glue

A strong glue which is quicker drying than PVA. (It would be ideal, for example, for sticking the magnets on to the plaster fish, see page 31.)

Wallpaper paste

This is a useful glue for sticking large areas of paper together for displays, etc. Make sure that the paste does not contain anti-fungal chemicals, as these are poisonous.

Glue gun

Do not use a hot temperature glue gun. Cool temperature glue guns are very useful but must be used with care. These low temperature glue guns are not hot enough to really burn, but still hot enough to be unpleasant.

FOOD HYGIENE

Before starting any cooking or tasting activity, children should tie back long hair, wash their hands with soap and water and cover any cuts with waterproof dressings. Work surfaces should be covered with a clean plastic sheet, kept especially for cooking. This should be wiped down by the teacher with a disinfectant. Children should wear aprons that are kept only for cooking.

If you do not have a sink reserved for cooking, then a special washing-up bowl should be kept for this purpose.

AIM OF PROJECT: To design and make harvest bread

RESOURCES
A wide variety of breads, including some from other cultures
Small clear bottles, yeast, balloons (for investigating)
Wheat grains, two clean large stones or a mortar and pestle for grinding the grain, hand lenses, saucers
Different wheat flours - wholemeal, granary, white, unbleached white, plain - and a variety of seeds: poppy,
sesame, sunflower
Oil for baking sheets, yeast, salt, sugar, egg
Mixing bowls, wooden spoons, jugs, scales, baking sheets, sieves, aprons

STARTING POINTS
- Have a selection of breads available for the children to examine: white, brown, wholemeal, matzos, crispbread, hallah plaited loaves. Include breads from other cultures such as pitta (Greece), naan (India), ciabatta (Italy), pumpernickel (Germany), baguette (France), soda bread (Ireland). Encourage the children to smell and taste the breads. Give them opportunities to explore the texture and appearance of each type of bread, as well as the similarities and the differences.
- Talk about bread and find out what the children already know about the ingredients of bread, and how it is made.
- Talk about Harvest Festival and the shapes of bread made to celebrate this time of year. Also look at other celebration breads: Chinese New Year bread in the shape of a fish, New Year pretzels from Germany, festive Breton bread, etc. Explain to the children that they are going to design and make their own festive bread.

INVESTIGATIONS

- What is bread made from? Show the children the grains of wheat and let them examine them carefully using a hand lens. Are the grains hard or soft?

- How does wheat grow? Place some grains in a flat dish or saucer with a little water and observe them as they germinate.

- In what season is wheat planted? What does it need in order to grow? In what season is it harvested? How is it harvested?

- How is flour made from wheat? Try grinding the wheat between two stones. Observe what happens to the grains. Introduce the words *millstone* and *mill*. Find out about traditional and modern methods of grinding wheat.

- Let the children observe the ground wheat and compare it with white flour and wholemeal flour. Which is their own ground wheat most similar to? What has been taken out of the white flour? Why?

- Let the children sieve their ground wheat to separate the flour from the bran. Observe bread made from wholemeal flour and bread made from white flour. Discuss which is healthier, and consider the reasons why.

- What else is in flour? Introduce the words *starch* and *gluten*. Let the children put a few spoons of flour into a bowl and mix it with some water into a dough. Take a basin of water and knead the dough in the water. What happens to the water? Why does the water become cloudy? Explain that the cloudiness is due to the starch dissolving in the water.

- Suggest that the children leave the cloudy water to evaporate in a warm place, and observe the starch left behind as a white powder.

- Why does the dough become more stretchy as the children knead it in the water? Explain that kneading the dough activates the gluten, and that gluten is elastic and enables the dough to expand and stretch.

We put yeast, warm water and a bit of sugar into a bottle and stretched a balloon over the neck of the bottle. After a while the balloon inflated.

Yeast

- How does bread rise? Show the children some yeast and explain that it is a living organism, a tiny fungus. Experiment by putting approximately three tablespoons of warm water in a clear bottle and then adding half a teaspoon of yeast and a pinch of sugar. Put a balloon on top of the bottle and leave it in a warm place. What happens to the balloon? Why? Explain that the yeast has produced a gas, carbon dioxide. Discuss how this gas makes the bread rise. The yeast produces carbon dioxide, which expands and stretches the dough, and so the dough rises.

- Does dough rise without kneading? Experiment and find out.

- Describe how dough changes when heated. Consider changes in colour, size, shape and texture.

- Discuss which of these changes are reversible and irreversible.

ASSIGNMENTS
To design and make harvest bread

Designing
- Collect ideas and images about harvest. Encourage children to visit the school library to find pictures of wheat sheaves, tractors, windmills, baskets, fruit, vegetables, etc., for inspiration. Encourage them to consider how they would like to represent Harvest Festival, and discuss what sort of loaf they would like to make. They could sketch their designs.

Making
- Remind the children about hygiene issues when working with food: wash hands, tie back long hair, wear aprons and clean down working area (it is best for an adult to wipe the area with a sterilizing solution). Introduce the children to the basic recipe.

BREAD
675g (1lb 8oz) plain flour
1 sachet easy-blend dried yeast
1 tsp salt
400ml (13 fl.oz) warm water
1 egg (for glazing)

Turn the oven on to 200°C.

Place the flour in a bowl, then mix in the yeast and salt. Make a well in the centre of the flour and pour the water in. Mix to a dough. If too sticky, add more flour. If too dry, add more water. Knead it well.

Shape the dough and leave it to rise in a warm place until double in size. Brush carefully with a beaten egg. This is a glaze and will give the loaf a good colour and shine when it is baked. Carefully place the loaf on a greased baking tray (it might be best to shape the loaf on the baking tray, as then it will not have to be moved), and bake in the preheated oven for 20-30 minutes.

NOTE: Strong flour would normally be used for bread-making, but as the dough becomes very elastic and difficult to work with (because of the high gluten content), plain flour is better for dough that needs to be shaped.

- Working in groups of two or three, the children should weigh and measure the ingredients and take turns to mix the dough. They will find that as they knead the dough, it becomes more and more elastic and more difficult to knead. Explain that this is because the gluten is being activated.

- When the dough is ready, the children can try to roll it into sausage shapes. As the dough will now be very elastic, this will need a lot of effort. Encourage the children to use words to describe the forces that they are using: *squeezing, pushing, pulling, twisting, stretching, rolling, flattening.*
- They can model shapes from it and plait and weave the rolled pieces together. Encourage them to refer to their designs as they proceed. The dough will keep rising as they work, so that by the time their loaf is ready, it will probably be fully risen. Remind the children that the bread will continue expanding in the oven, so they must leave ample room to allow for this on the baking tray.
- Finally, the children can measure and compare the length, width, height and weight of their loaf before and after baking. They can glaze the loaf with a beaten egg and sprinkle it with seeds (poppy, sesame, etc.) before baking, if desired.

EVALUATION
- How did the bread look on both the outside and inside after baking? How did it taste?
- Compare how it changed in length, width, height, weight, colour, shape and texture after baking.

EXTENSION ACTIVITIES
- Talk about nutrition and how we need a variety of foods to keep healthy.
- Ask the children to make a 'healthy food pyramid' poster, using old packaging and pictures from magazines, or using the database on the computer.

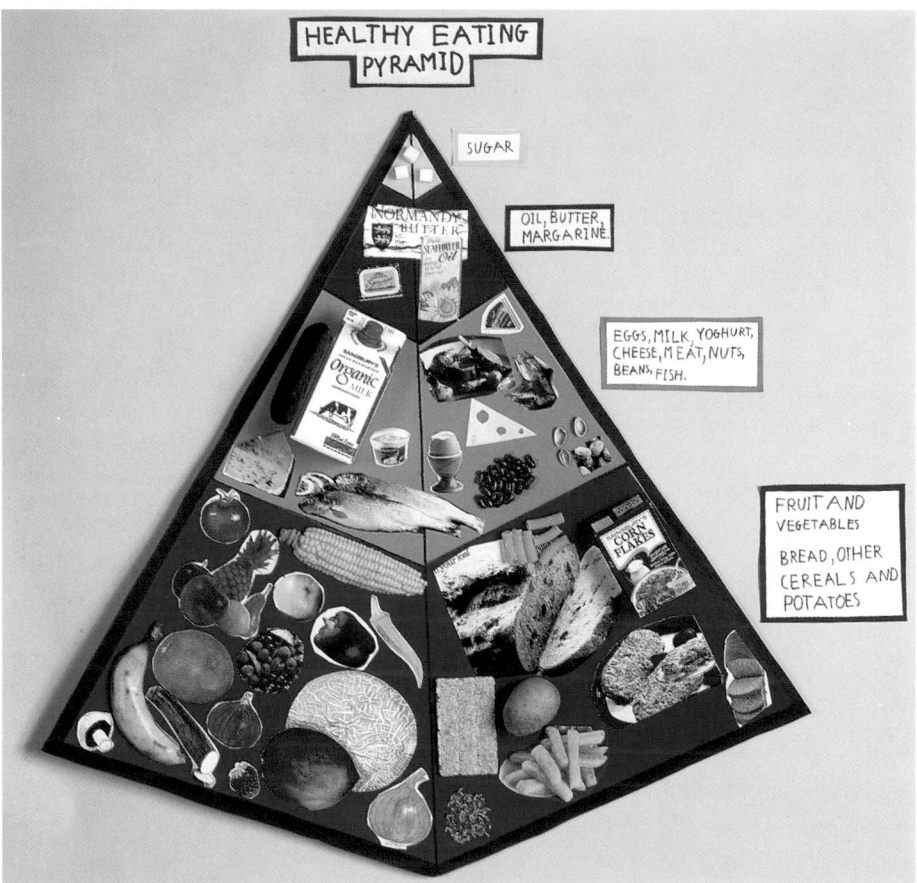

LANGUAGE OPPORTUNITIES
- Collect different recipes for bread and consider the way that they are set out sequentially. How are they written? Focus on the instructional text, the way that the ingredients are listed, followed by the method - sometimes set out as numbered points.
- Ask the children to write out their bread recipe, concentrating on the above points.
- Suggest that the children prepare a presentation of their work about bread for another class.

Teacher's notes: Gluten is very elastic and stretches easily, and this is why bread dough is able to rise. The starch in the flour provides the carbohydrate. The brown crust on the bread is the starch sugar which has become caramelised.

AIM OF PROJECT: To design and make a paper bridge to support 3000g

RESOURCES
A variety of different sorts of paper including tissue paper, display paper, sugar paper, craft paper, newspaper
Large cardboard box for bridge display
Adhesive tape, masking tape, PVA glue, glue brushes, glue stick
A selection of weights ranging from 10g to 1kg

STARTING POINTS
• Talk about bridges and find out what the children already know. Why do we have bridges? What do designers need to consider when they are designing bridges?
• Can a bridge be made from paper? Talk about paper. Where does it come from? How is it made?
• Consider whether paper can support a weight.

INVESTIGATIONS
• Let the children examine lots of different types of paper. How are they different? How are they the same? Are some easier to cut, fold or crumple than others? Why? Encourage them to devise a test to find out.
• What can the children make with paper by folding, cutting or tearing it? Let them explore different techniques such as fringing, curling by pulling over the edge of a table, rolling around a pencil, crumpling, tearing, weaving, twisting, pleating. Let them try out all the techniques for themselves.

- How easy is it to crumple a piece of paper? Now roll a piece the same size into a tube. Is it harder to crumple? Why? Demonstrate how rolling paper into tubes makes it much stronger.

- Show the children that by taping straws to paper they can make the paper stiffer. They can make their own straws by rolling paper around a cylinder shape.

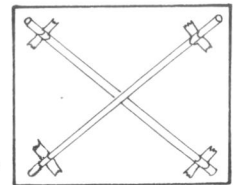

straws taped to paper

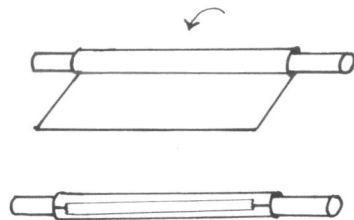

- Explain that the diameter of their straw or tube will depend on what they have rolled their paper around: pencil, rolling pin, dowel.

- Can a sheet of paper stand up? What if you fold it in half? Can you balance a pencil on top of the paper?

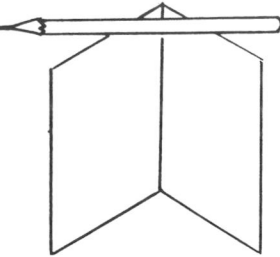

- Consider which techniques strengthen paper and which techniques are decorative.

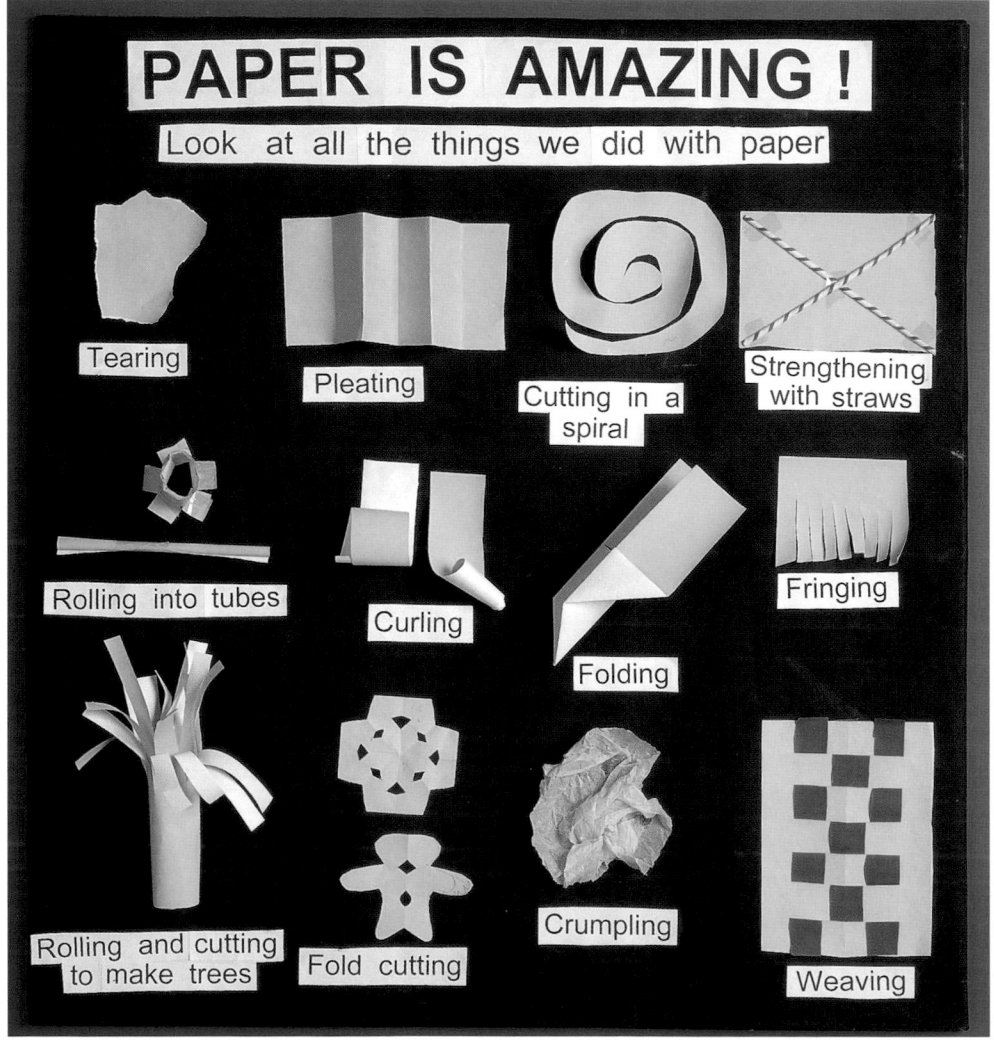

- Children can design and make a display board showing the results of their explorations and discussion. Encourage them to make the display visually stimulating and to use appropriate labels for the lettering. How can they make their lettering easy to read?

- Experiment with building a bridge made from paper. The children can decide the length they want their bridge to be and place two construction bricks or wooden blocks that distance apart. A piece of paper can be laid across the bricks and a small weight placed on the paper. What happens? Why? Place supports, i.e. two more blocks, to hold the paper down. What happens to the weight on the paper now? Why?

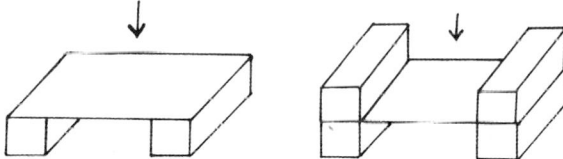

- Explain that everything experiences a pulling force towards the earth. This is the force of attraction that is known as *gravity*.

- Encourage the children to think about the upward forces as well as the downward forces, i.e. the downward forces must be balanced by upward forces: in this instance, so that the bridge does not collapse.

- Try adding supports under the paper bridge. Will it hold more weight now?

- Devise a test to find out if paper of different thicknesses, for example, tissue paper and sugar paper, hold more or less weight. If the paper is made stiffer by taping straws on to it, will the bridge hold more weight? Test it. Encourage the children to predict what they think will happen before they test it.

ASSIGNMENTS
To design and make a paper bridge that will support 3000g

Designing
- Fill a carrier bag with bags of flour/sugar to 3000g and let the children pick it up and feel the weight.

- Ask the children to consider what they have learned about making paper stiffer, and about making paper supports. Can they design a bridge that will support 3000g in weight using this knowledge? Let them make sketches of their ideas.

- Let the children decide on the length of their bridge before they start making it.

- Design a possible landscape around the bridge.

Making
- Explain to the children that they are going to make a bridge (across a river or road) that will hold 3000g in weight. Provide the children with a good cross-section of weights, from small weights up to maximum 1kg.

- How will they strengthen the paper for their bridge? How will they secure the ends of their bridge? Will their bridge need support and, if so, how will they make the supports?

- If they are making a landscape, they could use a backdrop or a box, and make animals and people from folded paper. If you want to use the bridge for display purposes, the test to breaking point would have to be postponed!

- Once their bridge is finished and dry, they can put weights carefully onto the bridge, adding up the total weight as they go along.

NOTE: The children working on this particular project decided that they wanted a high bridge, so they chose two cardboard boxes for the 'banks' of the river. They were asked to make the crossing section out of paper, and they discovered that it needed to be strengthened. They used two crossed straws taped to the back, and strengthened around the edges with further straws. The children then decided to make upright supports for their bridge with rolled paper (see photograph on page 13).

EVALUATION

• Did your bridge hold 3000g? If it did, congratulate yourselves and identify its strengths.

• Did your bridge break? How much weight did it hold before it collapsed? Were you able to identify the reasons, and improve your design?

• Are you pleased with your landscape design around the bridge?

EXTENSION ACTIVITIES

• Find out about arch bridges. Examine how the curve of the arch spreads the load on the bridge and makes it stronger than the beam bridge.

• Take two halves of an eggshell. Let the children feel one half. Is it strong? How thick is it? Does it crush easily? Place the other half in a shallow tray with a layer of sand in it. Put a piece of card on top of the eggshell and place weights on it (the card might need a bit of Blu-Tack to stop it from sliding off the shell). Does the eggshell crush easily now? Why not?

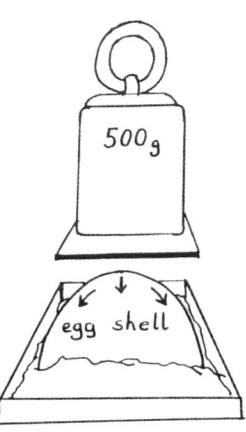

LANGUAGE OPPORTUNITIES

• Compare a range of story settings and select words and phrases that describe scenes involving landscapes.

• Write a story setting for your particular landscape and bridge.

Teacher's notes: A bridge is a structure that joins the span between a river, road, valley, ravine, etc. There are three main types of bridges:

Beam bridge   **Arch bridge**   **Suspension bridge**

LET THE LIGHT SHINE

AIM OF PROJECT: To design and make a stable candlestick using clay

RESOURCES
Construction kits to explore the building of tall shapes
Air drying clay (make sure this is soft and malleable; if not, it is very
   difficult to work with)
Paint and brushes of different sizes, PVA glue
Small, heavy metal objects (ball bearings, nuts, curtain weights) to push
   into the base of the clay if needed
Lolly sticks
Candles

STARTING POINTS
* Why do we use candles (for light, to celebrate)? Consider times past.
* This is a good opportunity to talk about the different celebrations and festivals where candles are used,
  such as Hanukah, Divali, Christmas, birthdays.
* Talk about safety with lighted candles and the need for candle holders. Why not just hold them in our
  hands? What would happen if a candlestick holding a lit candle fell over?
* Collect as many candlesticks as possible for the children to examine. Ask the children and teachers to
  bring one in each to get as broad a selection as possible.
* Encourage the children to look at the shapes, feel them, put candles in them. Do some fall over more
  easily than others? Why? Give the children lots of time to examine the structures, and encourage their
  exploration with questions. Are some of the candlesticks heavier or wider at their base than others? Why?
* Explain to the children that they are going to design and make their own candle holder using clay.

INVESTIGATIONS
Centre of gravity

• Let the children build tall towers using construction kits. What do you notice about the tower as it becomes taller? Why does it fall over? Can you prevent it from falling over? How?

• Explain to the children that the force of gravity is always acting on the earth, and gravity pulls objects down towards the earth.

• Show them how to find the 'centre of gravity' of their tower by balancing it on their finger, or on a lolly stick. The point of balance is the centre of gravity.

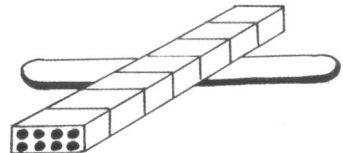

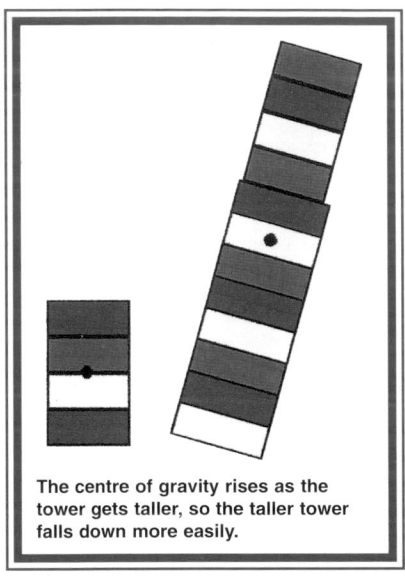

The centre of gravity rises as the tower gets taller, so the taller tower falls down more easily.

• Explain that the centre of gravity rises as the tower becomes taller. As the centre of gravity moves further away from the base of the tower, the tower becomes unstable and falls.

• Investigate what happens if the children put a base on the tower, or add supports, or put a weight at the bottom.

• Develop the use of appropriate vocabulary as they explore stability and instability: *tall, unstable, moving, wobbly, shaky, unbalanced, falling, unsteady, short, stable, still, secure, firm, balanced, sturdy,* etc.

• The children can make a display board of their findings.

Changing materials

- Put a candle into a candle holder and light it. Invite the children to observe closely what happens. Encourage them to write down all the things they observe, in the correct sequence.

- What happens to the wax as it burns? Does it change? What happens to the melted wax? Is this wax a liquid? Why does it become solid again? What happens to the wick as it burns?

- Blow the candle out and, once it is cool, ask the children to examine the cooled down wax and wick. How have they changed? Consider the changes which are reversible (i.e. the cooled wax), or irreversible (i.e. the burnt wick).

ASSIGNMENTS
To design and make a stable candlestick using clay

Designing

- Ask the children to design a candlestick which they would like to make. Encourage them to consider all the things they found out about stability and the centre of gravity in their investigating. Let them use their construction kit models as a guide. Explain to them that labelling their designs will make them clearer.

- Ask them to look at each other's designs and see if they can understand them.

Children's designs for their candlesticks

Making

- Encourage the children to plan the order in which they are going to make their candlesticks. Explain that the clay will need time to dry (at least a day) before it is ready to be painted. Let them cover their work surfaces with protective coverings such as dustsheets or newspaper before starting. Remind them to wear aprons.

- Teach the children how to use 'clay glue' (i.e. slip) to stick the clay together (see Techniques, page 6).

- As the children make their candlesticks, encourage them to continually evaluate how stable the structure is. Does it fall over easily? How can they make it more stable?

- Let them try squashing heavy metal pieces such as nuts and bolts, steel bearings, etc., into the soft clay base. Does this make it more stable? Why?

- How will they make the part to hold the candle? How will they get it the right size? Encourage them to brainstorm ideas and to try out different ways. Suggest that they press the end of a candle into a small ball of clay and attach it to their model.

- Encourage the children to describe the forces they are exerting on the clay, for example, *twisting, stretching, squashing, squeezing, pushing, pulling, rolling, flattening.*

- Once their candlesticks are dry, they are ready to be painted. Encourage the children to plan their painting and their choice of colours carefully before they start. Explain that by starting with the lightest colours first, and then using progressively darker ones, the colours will always show up well.

- When the paint is dry, explain to the children how they can varnish their work with thinned-down PVA glue.

EVALUATION

Allow the children to evaluate their finished work by considering:

        Are the candlesticks stable?
        Do they hold the candles?
        Would they be safe to use?
        Do they look good?

EXTENSION ACTIVITY

- Find the centre of gravity of an uneven shape.

 **1. Using a paper drill, make two holes in an uneven shape cut from card.**

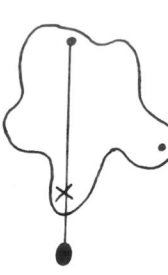 **2. Use a nail to hang shape from one of the holes, and then hang a plumb line (string with a blob of clay on one end) onto the nail. Mark a cross on the plumb line. Join the cross and the hole with a straight line. Repeat this procedure with the second hole.**

 **3. The point where the two lines cross is the centre of gravity. Try to balance the shape on your finger on this point.**

LANGUAGE OPPORTUNITIES

- Design a poster for the safe use of candles.

- Using the computer, the children could produce neat and detailed instructions, together with diagrams, showing how the centre of gravity changed as their towers became taller.

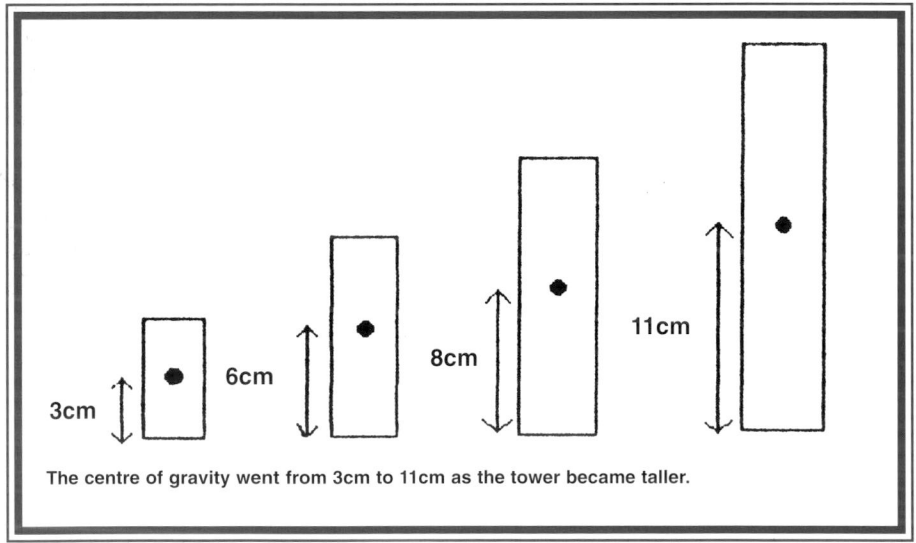

The centre of gravity went from 3cm to 11cm as the tower became taller.

Teacher's notes:
- The centre of gravity is the point at which the whole weight of an object balances.
- The centre of gravity should be kept low in order to achieve stability.

AIM OF PROJECT: To design and make a clock equivalent to their own height for the nursery rhyme 'Hickory, Dickory, Dock'

RESOURCES

Many cardboard boxes of different sizes

Gummed paper (for collage)

Gummed tape, bowls of water and sponges for wetting the gummed paper and tape

PVA glue

Sand/stones

Hole punches or paper drills

String, wire, cotton reels, cardboard tubes and small boxes for making winches

Pliers for cutting wire

Masking tape to protect ends of wire

Paints and a variety of brushes

Textiles (felt and fur fabric) to make mice

Books with illustrations of the nursery rhyme 'Hickory, Dickory, Dock'

Pictures of grandfather clocks

Construction kits

STARTING POINTS

- Read 'Hickory, Dickory, Dock' to the children and look at different books showing illustrations of the rhyme. Compare the different illustrations. Are the clocks all the same?
- Look at other pictures of grandfather clocks. How are they different? How are they the same?
- Discuss making a clock as tall as the children themselves with a moving mouse.
- Let the children measure each other and record their heights.

INVESTIGATIONS
Winding mechanisms

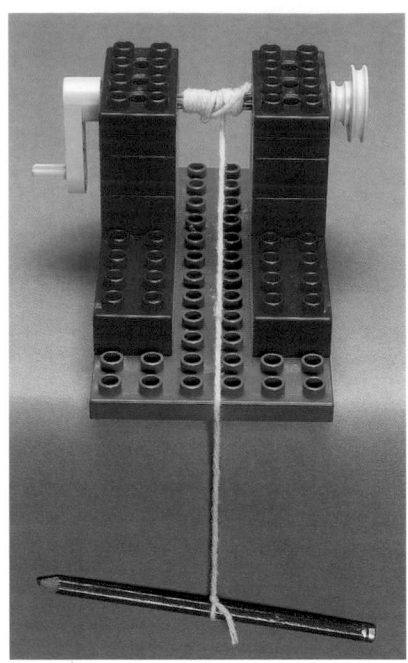

- Explain that a winch is a machine and that machines all have parts that work together and are driven by some form of power.

- The children can start by experimenting with making winding mechanisms using construction kits, if these are available.

- They can tie one end of a length of string on to the winding mechanism and tie a weight (for example, a pencil) on to the other end. Does the pencil wind up? If not, why? Encourage the children to observe closely what happens when the handle is turned. Should the string be taped rather than tied onto the winding mechanism?

- Let the children make their own winding mechanism (introducing the word winch) using wire and small boxes. (Show them how to cover the cut ends of the wire with masking tape, as they can be very sharp.)

- They will need to punch holes into two opposite sides of the box for the wire to go through. Point out that the holes need to be in line, i.e. parallel with the front of the box, otherwise the handle will not turn properly. Let the children explore what happens if the holes punched into the box are not parallel.

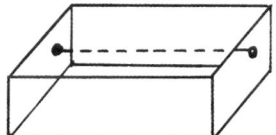

- Demonstrate how to bend the wire for the handle, using pliers. Younger children might need support to do this.

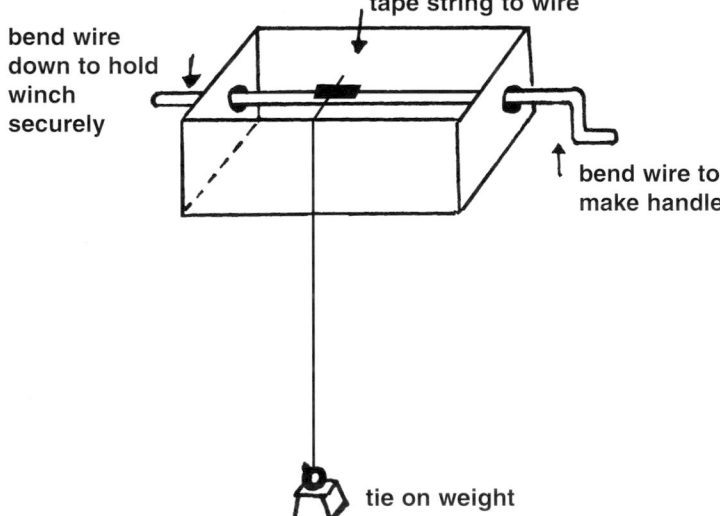

bend wire down to hold winch securely

tape string to wire

bend wire to make handle

tie on weight

- Show the children how to tape one end of a length of string to the wire and add a small weight on to the other end of the string. Investigate how many times the handle has to be turned to wind up the weight. Try different weights.

- Let them try putting a cotton reel onto their wire. Explain that they will need to make sure that the cotton reel is firmly taped to the wire, so that it will turn when the handle is turned.

- Let them tape their length of string (with the weight on one end), to the cotton reel drum, and wind the weight up again. How many times did you have to turn the handle this time? Was it more or less than with just the wire? Why? Ask the children to make sketches of their winches.

- The children can investigate the effects of making winches using cardboard tubes with different diameters.

- Make a resource board for the school to share the children's discoveries.

Structures
- Let the children use the cardboard boxes to build a tall tower. Why do the towers fall over as they get higher?

- Try towers with big boxes at the bottom and smaller ones at the top. Try towers with small boxes at the bottom and bigger ones on top. Which tower stands up better? Why?

ASSIGNMENTS
To design and make a clock equivalent to their own height, for the nursery rhyme 'Hickory, Dickory, Dock'

Designing
- Let the children explore and develop their ideas through assembling and rearranging the boxes, and consider their designs as they develop.
- How do you think that you will arrange your boxes to make a tall clock?
- They can hold the boxes together with temporary fixings like Blu-Tack and masking tape.
- The children will need to decide where they will put their winch. Will they open up a box in the top of their clock? Will they glue it to the side or back of the box? How will they make the string go to the front of the clock? Let them try out their ideas and get the string to wind up in the front of the clock.
- How will they make their mice?
- Collect ideas for the decoration of the clocks.

The Ndebele live in South Africa.
They paint their houses with geometric patterns. geometric
They use bright colours on the outside walls.
Inside they use earth colours.
We used their ideas to design pattens for our clocks
Kayleigh
Maia
Aaron
Chantal
Alex

NOTE: For the clocks shown in the photograph above, the children looked at photographs of the decorated houses of the Ndebele people of Southern Africa.

- The children can make drawings of their designs and displays showing the source of their inspiration and how their designs evolved.

Making

- Show the children how to stick their boxes together by putting lots of PVA glue between the boxes and then using short strips of gummed tape around the edges of the boxes to get a good join.
- Once the clocks have been stuck together and have dried, the children can start painting (or, as in the examples in the photograph on page 21, create a collage using coloured paper). Let them experiment painting on different scraps of card. What happens to light colours like yellow? Is this the effect you want? How can you get a bright effect? Let them try the same colours on a white background. Do you like these colours better? Suggest that they cover the whole clock in white paint and let it dry to give a good base.
- Have a selection of collage materials available for the children to select for making their mice.
- Encourage the children to evaluate their work as they proceed, and to identify strengths and weaknesses. Does the clock fall over? Is the bottom wide enough? Should it be heavier? Would putting stones or sand into the bottom box make a difference? What is the best position for the winding mechanism? Can you turn the handle from this position?
- Tape the winch to its position and make a hole in the front of the clock for the string to be threaded through. Tie the mouse onto the end of the string.
- Does the mouse go up and down? If not, why? Is the mouse too heavy or too light?

• Let the children use a graphics program on the computer to design patterns for their clocks.

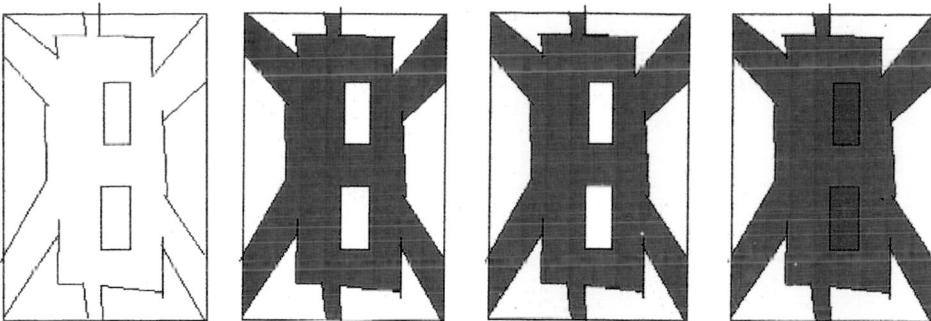

• Different colourways can be explored.

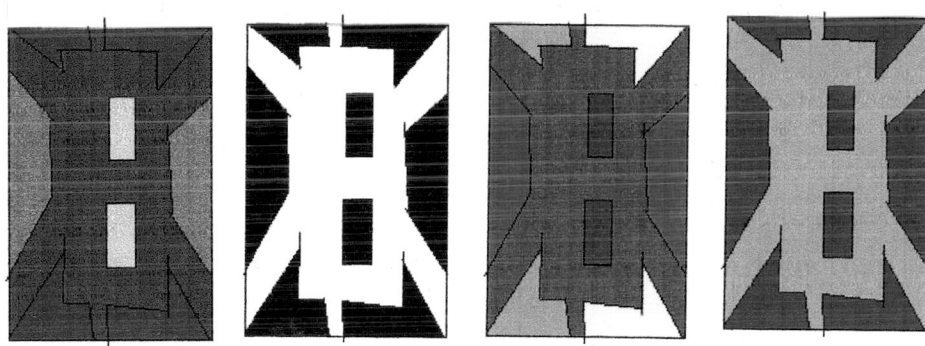

NOTE: After looking carefully at the Ndebele patterns the children had chosen for inspiration to decorate their clocks, they drew their patterns freehand with the mouse using computer graphics. They printed and saved their designs as they progressed, and so had a layout that showed the process of their designs (see examples above).

EVALUATION

• Test your winch to see if the mouse runs up the clock.

• Can you work your winch in time with saying the nursery rhyme, 'Hickory, Dickory, Dock'?

• Is your clock stable? If not, how can you make it more stable?

• Are you pleased with the decoration of your clock?

EXTENSION ACTIVITY

• Let the children explore simple pulleys. They can use their winch mechanisms with a simple pulley and attach a weight of 250g. Does it pull up easily? Experiment with different weights.

LANGUAGE OPPORTUNITIES

• Encourage the children to make lists of the rhyming words from the nursery rhyme 'Hickory, Dickory, Dock' in order to substitute their own words and ideas, and write new lines for the poem.

• Read other rhymes and poems to collect and categorise favourite ones to create a class anthology.

> **Teacher's notes:** A winch is a simple machine consisting of a drum with rope or string that can be turned around it using a handle.

A BRIGHT IDEA

AIM OF PROJECT: To design and make a model which has a light that can be controlled by a switch

RESOURCES
1.5AA batteries
Battery tester
A selection of battery holders to hold one battery, two batteries and four batteries
Crocodile leads
Small light bulbs in a variety of voltages from 1.5v to 4.5v
A variety of materials, both metal and non-metal, to test for conductors and insulators
Drawing pins, split pins, paper clips, aluminium foil for switches
Wire strippers
A low temperature glue gun (to attach battery and bulb holder to model)
A selection of boxes, tubes, newspaper, etc.
PVA glue, masking tape, paint, brushes
NOTE: Warn of the dangers of mains electricity. Do not use rechargeable batteries.

STARTING POINTS
• Discuss different appliances that use electricity. What do the children have at home that uses electricity? Is it battery-powered or mains-powered? Which room is it in? Which room in their home do they think has the most electrical appliances? Ask the children to conduct a survey at home to find out, and make a bar chart of the result. Have children noticed where the switches are in their homes? Why are they different in bathrooms?
• **Talk to the children about the dangers of electricity.** Explain that the batteries they will be using are quite safe, unless they are damaged.

INVESTIGATIONS
• Provide sets of 1.5v batteries and holders, 1.5v bulbs and holders, and two crocodile leads. Let the children work singly or in pairs. Give them ample time to examine all the components.

- Explain that electricity flows from the battery through the wires and the bulb and back to the battery. This is a circuit, the path which electricity takes as it flows. A switch can control electrical flow.
- Let the children find the + and - signs on the battery. Explain that these are the positive and negative terminals and that the flow of electricity from the negative to the positive makes the bulb light up.
- Give the children plenty of time to explore making a circuit on their own. If they find it difficult, prompt them with questions like "What if....." and so encourage them to explore and experiment further.

- When their circuit is complete, the children can make a drawing of it. Encourage them to show the + and - on their drawings.

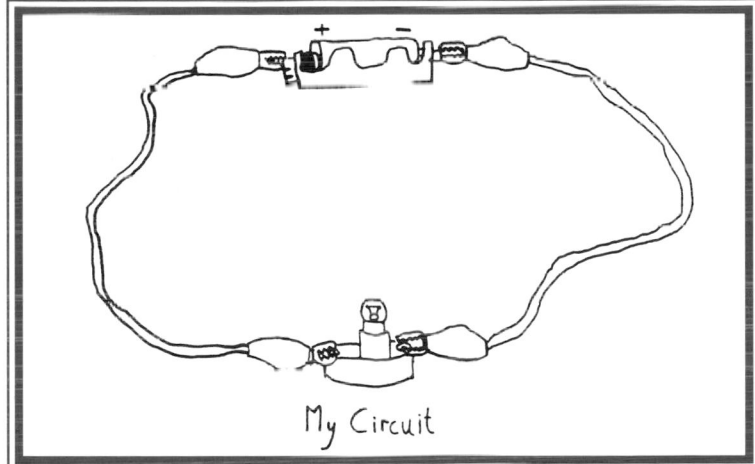

NOTE: Whilst it is accepted that electricity actually flows from negative to positive terminals it is conventionally shown as flowing from positive to negative.

- How bright is the light? How could we make it brighter? Provide the children with battery holders that hold two and four batteries. What happens when you put two batteries into the circuit? Does it become brighter or dimmer? What happens if you put in four batteries? Why?
- Explain that 1.5v bulbs will have a short life if used with 3v batteries because the metal coil in the bulb (the filament) will overheat and melt, and the circuit will then be broken. Let the children examine the filament through a hand lens. Show them how to use the correct battery power for the bulbs voltage, i.e.

Battery	Bulb
1.5v	1.5v
3v	2.5v
4.5v	3.5v

- Let the children disconnect one of the leads. What happens? Why? How can you make the electricity flow again? Investigate placing different materials, both metal and non-metal, between two points in the circuit, to see which allows the current to flow through and light the bulb. Sort these into conductors and insulators.

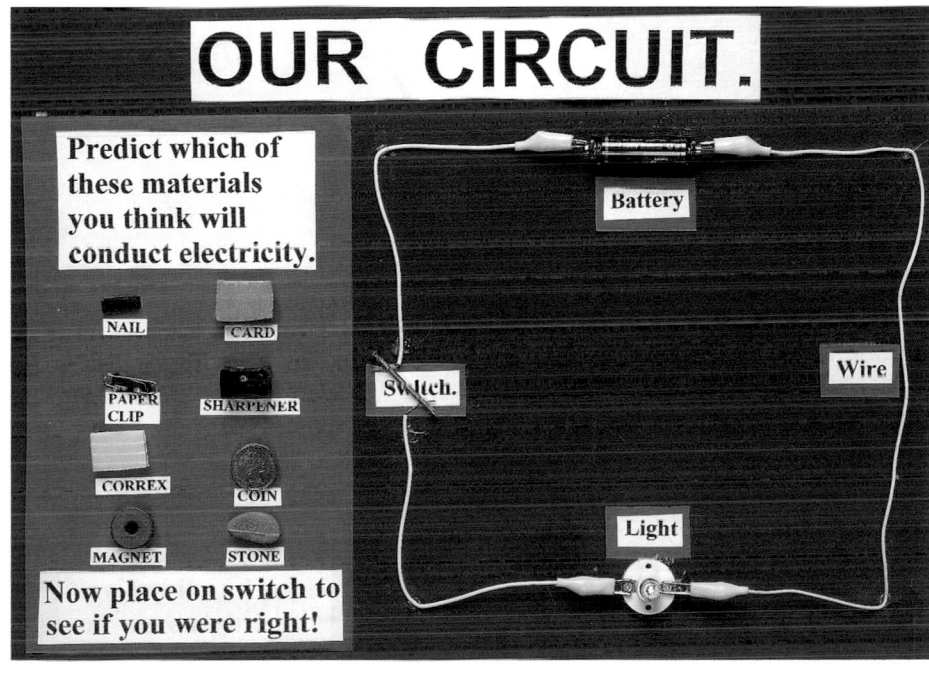

- The children can make a display board to show materials which conduct electricity and materials which do not.

- The children can hold hands in a circle and become a 'circuit'. Who will be the battery? Who will be the bulb? the motor? the buzzer? Who will be the switch? The rest can be the wires. When everyone holds hands, the circuit is complete, the electricity flows, and the bulb lights up. Squeeze hands to represent the passage of electricity around the circuit. What happens if they let go hands so that there is a break in the circuit?

- Explore how a switch works in a simple circuit. The children can make their own switches for their circuit.

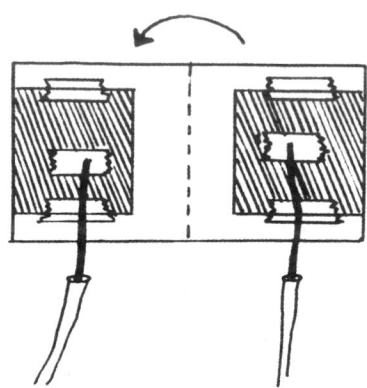

Tape two squares of aluminium foil to a piece of card with adhesive tape. Tape stripped wires on to the foil. When the card is folded over, the circuit is connected.

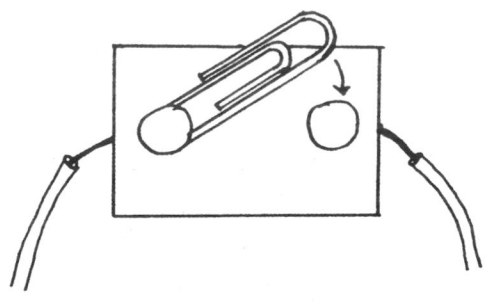

Push two split pins into a small square of cardboard or corrugated plastic.
Loop stripped wires around the split pins and hook the paper clip around one of the split pins. When the paper clip touches the second split pin, the circuit is connected.

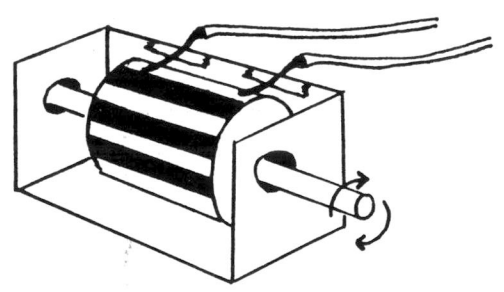

This switch makes a flashing light
Tape card circles over the ends of a tube and make holes to push dowel or a pencil through. Tape strips of aluminium foil lengthways onto the tube and push the dowel or pencil through holes in a box as illustrated. Tape wires to the back of the box, making sure that the stripped ends of the wire can touch the tube as the tube is turned. When the wires touch the foil, the circuit is completed. When they touch the card of the tube, the circuit is broken, so that as the tube is turned, the light flashes on and off.

ASSIGNMENTS
To design and make a model which has a light that can be controlled by a switch

Designing
- Decide on a suitable model to make. Sketch out ideas for the design.

- Present the children with recycled materials (cardboard boxes, tubes, newspaper) to make their model. Let them choose materials from a large variety available to them. Encourage them to use the materials and temporary fastening (like masking tape) to assemble and design the model. If they decide to use tubes for their model, show them how to cut the tubes to give them a better sticking area (see Techniques, page 6).

- Encourage the children to explore and consider issues of stability, position of the light, position of the battery, and switch.

NOTE: The switch on this model has a drawing pin in the back of the finger. When this drawing pin touches the metal glasses the boy is wearing, the circuit is completed and the bulb lights up. When the hand is moved, the drawing pin no longer touches the metal glasses and so the circuit is broken.

- Ask the children to plan their circuit for their model. Older children could use a computer to design their circuit.

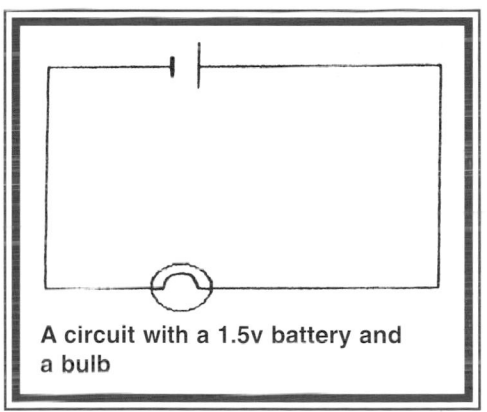

A circuit with a 1.5v battery and a bulb

Making

- Encourage the children to cover their working area with newspaper. Teach them how to glue their boxes, tubes etc. together using PVA on the joins and then sticking masking tape over the join to hold it together while it dries. (For round or oval shapes see techniques on page 6.) Explain that the glue will need to dry overnight.

- Once the glue is dry, show the children how to cover the whole model in newspaper strips painted with plenty of thinned down PVA glue (50/50 with water). Explain that they do not have to remove the masking tape, as the PVA is strong enough to stick over it. Again, they will have to wait until this is all dry.

- How strong is their model now?

- Let them try and paint with yellow paint on some scraps of white card and brown card. Does the paint show up on the brown card? Does it show up better on the white card? Why? Encourage them to paint their models completely white (especially if they plan to use light or pale shades) before they paint and decorate them. Remind them that they will have to wait for the white paint to dry before painting their models in their chosen colours.

- Finally, the children need to position and fix the circuit into their model. Encourage them to place everything carefully, and make sure that it all works and is correctly positioned before they attach the bulb holder and battery holder using a low temperature glue gun.

EVALUATION
- Does the bulb in your model light up? If not, can you find the fault? Is the battery flat? Use a battery tester to check. Is the bulb broken? Try another bulb. Check all the connections carefully. Does the switch work?

- How does your model look? How could you improve your design?

EXTENSION ACTIVITIES
- Provide small 1.5 to 3v motors, plastic pulleys (about 30mm diameter) and card discs.

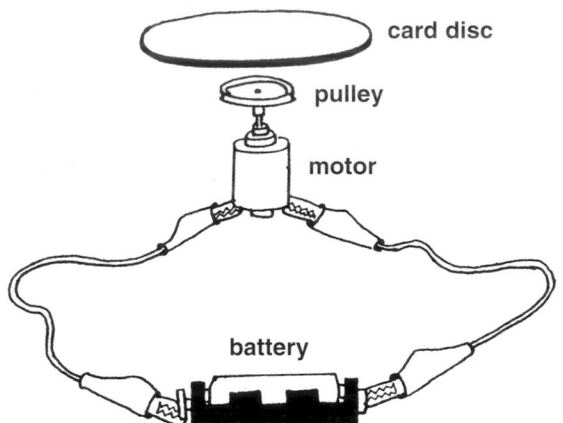

- Introduce the children to motors. Can they put a motor in their circuit instead of a light bulb? Let them push a plastic pulley onto the motor shaft. Explain that this will enable them to see the direction in which the motor spins. Does the motor spin clockwise or anti-clockwise? Let them swap the crocodile leads connected to their motor. Does the motor change direction?

- The children can attach decorated card discs to the pulleys using double-sided tape. What happens to the patterns on their disc when the motor spins? Let them try using several different colour combinations in decorating their discs. What happens to the colours when the motor spins? Try sticking a square piece of card on to the pulley. What happens when the square spins?

LANGUAGE OPPORTUNITIES
- Children can write a list of instructions to show how they made a simple electrical circuit, or how they made their model.
- Design an electricity safety poster or leaflet.

Teacher's notes: There are several different symbols used in circuit diagrams, for instance, a bulb can be represented as:

Let the children choose which symbol the class will use, and then stay with that symbol to avoid confusion.

Symbols
Batteries
Batteries are composed of 1.5 volt cells. A battery is made up of two or more 1.5v cells.

The symbol for a 1.5 volt cell (i.e. a 1.5v 'battery')

The symbol for a 3 volt battery (i.e. two 1.5 volt cells)

The symbol for a 4.5 volt battery (i.e. three 1.5 volt cells)

switch   motor   bulb   buzzer

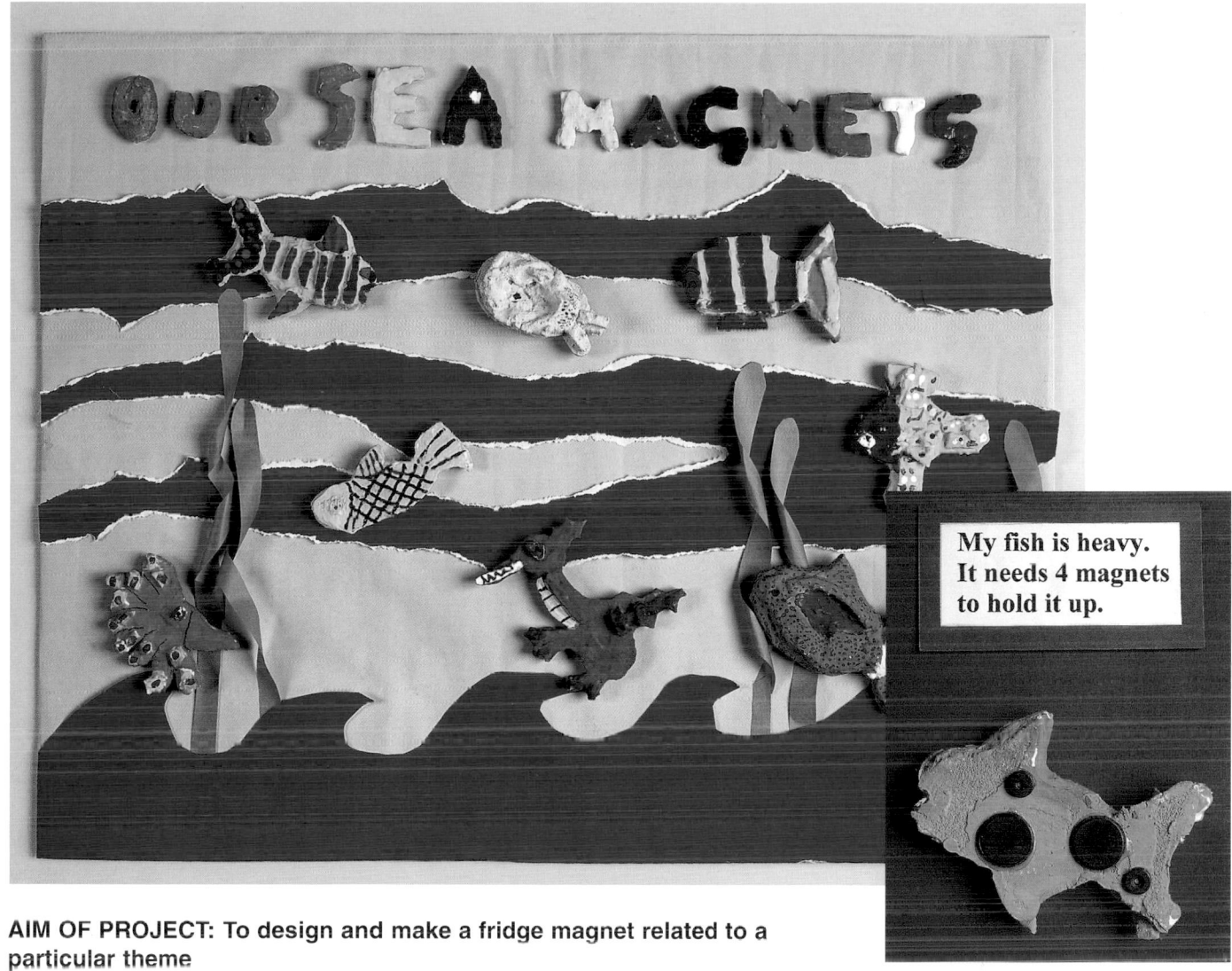

My fish is heavy.
It needs 4 magnets
to hold it up.

AIM OF PROJECT: To design and make a fridge magnet related to a particular theme

RESOURCES

Sheets of sponge, 5mm thick, or bath sponges cut into 5mm slices
Magnets, for testing - and to use in making
Plaster of Paris
Hand lenses
A variety of magnetic and non-magnetic materials
All-purpose solvent-free glue

Paint, brushes and felt-tip pens
Newspaper and dustsheets to protect surfaces
Disposable cups in which to mix plaster of Paris (for investigating)
Plastic bowl for mixing plaster of Paris (for making)
Plastic sheet or aluminium foil, aprons
Books with poems and stories on the chosen theme
Plastic bowls filled with water for washing hands

NOTE: Plaster of Paris must not be put down the sink as it blocks drains.

STARTING POINTS

• Ask the children to bring in fridge magnets from home. Let them examine the collection together. Do they stick to the wall? Do they stick to a metal surface? Will the magnet hold a piece of paper onto a metal surface? Will it hold a piece of card? a piece of plastic? Are they hard or soft? What sort of material are they made from? Explain to the children that magnets should not be placed near the computer monitor or screen.

• Let the children research and read aloud stories and poems about the topic on which they choose to work.

NOTE: In the example shown here, the children decided to make sea creatures, and observations were made of fish in a fish tank, and in reference books.

INVESTIGATIONS

Magnets

- Have a collection of materials, as well as magnets, available for the children to explore. What can a magnet do? Are all magnets the same shape? What kinds of materials are magnetic/non-magnetic? Are all metals magnetic? Ask the children to predict which materials are magnetic. Devise a test to find out.

- Encourage the children to record the results of their findings.

Changing materials

- Have small pieces of sponge available for the children to examine with a hand lens. Let the children dip sponges into water. What happens? Why? Squeeze the sponges. What happens? Talk about absorbent materials.

- Consider which materials are the easiest to cut: wood, plastic or sponge.

- The sponge is easy to cut, but it is soft. Can it be changed into a hard material?

- Show the children some plaster of Paris. Let them put a teaspoon of plaster of Paris into a tablespoon of water in a disposable cup, stir, and observe what happens over a period of half an hour. Why has it become solid?

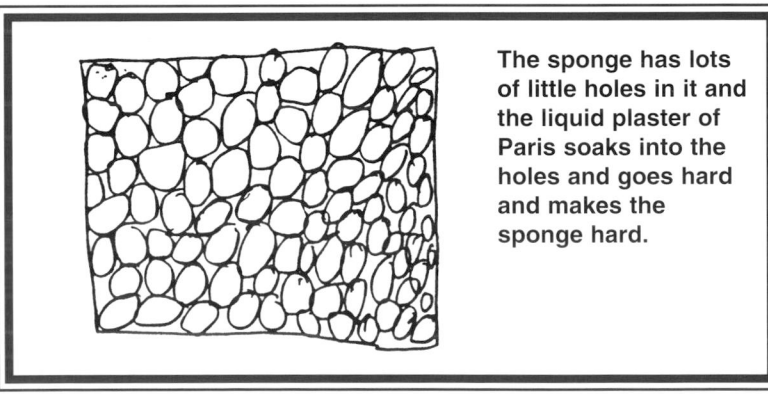

The sponge has lots of little holes in it and the liquid plaster of Paris soaks into the holes and goes hard and makes the sponge hard.

- Encourage them to make observations about the changes that take place when plaster of Paris is added to water. Why does the plaster get warm as it hardens? Can they devise a fair test to discover whether adding more or less plaster of Paris makes a difference to the strength of the plaster? Does the setting time change? Let them make predictions about the setting time required and test results.

- Mix another small batch of plaster of Paris and ask the children to dip and squeeze pieces of sponge into it. What happens? Encourage the children to record and sketch their observations.

Sponge has lots of holes

You can look through the magnifying glass to see the holes.

The sponge is soft.

Feel it.

We dipped our sponge into plaster-of-paris.

The sponge absorbed the plaster-of-paris.

When the sponge dried, it was hard.
You can feel it.

• Children can design and make a display board to record their discoveries.

ASSIGNMENTS
To design and make a fridge magnet related to a particular theme

Designing

• Ask the children to record their ideas for their chosen theme. Encourage them to think of colour, shape and pattern. What colours would look good together? Is the shape going to be possible to cut out? Will adding patterns improve the overall effect? Designs could be painted or sketched.

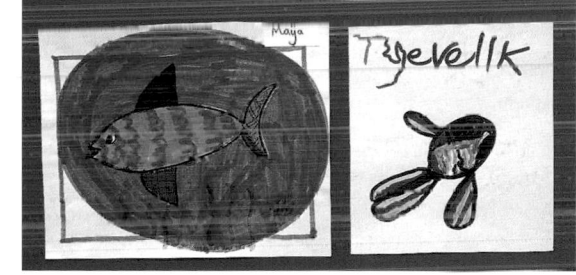

• Encourage the children to consider the size their magnet will be.

Making

• Using their designs as a guide, let the children select the sponge they wish to work with. The children should draw their designs onto the sponge using a felt-tip pen and cut them out.

• Plaster of Paris is messy. The children will need to cover the working area with sheets of newspaper, roll up sleeves, wear aprons and tie back long hair.

• Teach them how to mix plaster of Paris. Pour water into the plastic bowl to about a quarter of the depth, pour in the plaster until it forms a heap in the middle (to above water level), then mix until smooth.

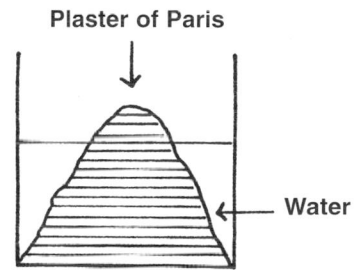

Plaster of Paris

Water

• **WARNING: Remind the children that when using plaster of Paris they must wash their hands in the bowls of water provided, and not in the sinks, because plaster will harden in the pipes.**

- Explain that the consistency needs to be like thin cream, so that the plaster can be absorbed into the holes of the sponge. Squeeze the sponge in the liquid plaster in order to get more plaster into the holes. If the plaster is too thick, it will just sit as a layer on the outside of the sponge and break off easily: two coats of thin plaster are better than one thick coat. Let the children take the sponges out and lay them on oiled plastic sheeting or aluminium foil. Explain that they can add pieces of sponge that have been dipped into the plaster, in order to create 3D effects.
- Remind the children that once the plaster starts to harden it cannot be used anymore and they will have to mix up a new batch.
- When the sponge designs are dry (overnight), the children can paint them and add detail with felt-tip pens. They can be varnished with a coat of PVA glue and water (mixed 50/50).
- The children will need to experiment to find the best position to attach their magnet to the back of their creation, and to decide whether one magnet will be enough to hold the weight. Once the correct position has been decided, attach the magnet using a strong glue.

EVALUATION
- Test your fridge magnet on a metal surface. Does it stay upright, or does it slide or fall down? Is your creation strong or is it brittle? Does it look good? Will it hold a piece of paper onto the surface? How could you improve it?

EXTENSION ACTIVITY
- Explore other changing materials, for example, water to ice, melting chocolate. Consider reversible and irreversible changes.

LANGUAGE OPPORTUNITIES
- Read through poetry which relates to the theme chosen for their magnets, in order to inspire the children's own poetry. Build up a word bank of suggested words (perhaps focusing on one particular aspect, for example, as in this project, the movement of the fish).
- Explore ways of presenting their poems using a computer - for example, enlarging, using bold and italics.

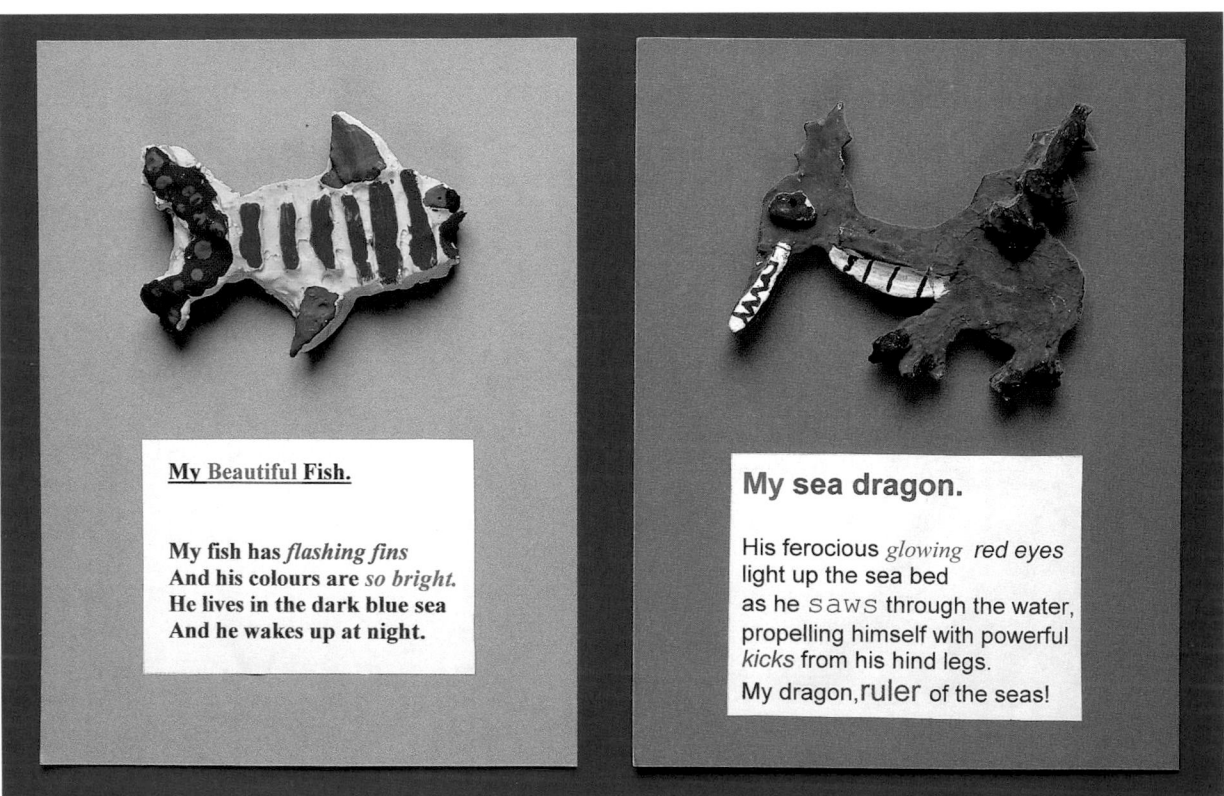

My Beautiful Fish.

My fish has *flashing fins*
And his colours are *so bright*.
He lives in the dark blue sea
And he wakes up at night.

My sea dragon.

His ferocious *glowing red eyes*
light up the sea bed
as he saws through the water,
propelling himself with powerful
kicks from his hind legs.
My dragon, ruler of the seas!

Teacher's notes:
When plaster of Paris is mixed with water, heat is released as part of the chemical reaction which takes place.

HUMPTY DUMPTY

AIM OF PROJECT: To design and make a falling Humpty Dumpty using pneumatic forces

RESOURCES
Balloons, syringes, squeezy bottles (such as empty washing-up bottles) for investigating
3mm and 5mm plastic tubing
Lots of small boxes of the same size (small cereal boxes, light bulb boxes) with which to build the wall
Paint, sand and sawdust (to add to paint to create textures for the wall)
Balloons, gummed tape, collage materials for Humpty Dumpty
PVA glue

STARTING POINTS
• Read and discuss the nursery rhyme, 'Humpty Dumpty'. Look at different representations of Humpty Dumpty. Let the children brainstorm ideas as to how they could make a model of the rhyme. How could they build the wall? How can they make Humpty Dumpty? How can they make him fall? How can they make him break open when he falls?

INVESTIGATIONS
• Inflate a balloon in front of the class. What happens when you let it go? Why is the balloon propelled around the room?

- Let the children experiment with balloons and squeezy bottles joined with 5mm tubing. What happens when you squeeze the bottle? Why does the balloon inflate? Where is the air coming from and how is it moving from the squeezy bottle to the balloon? Encourage them to make drawings of their discoveries.

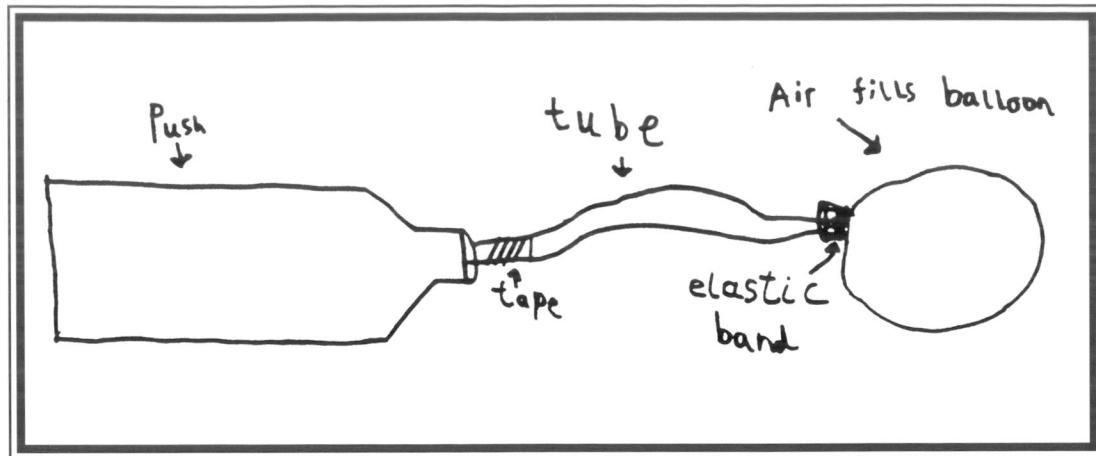

- Would this air-filled balloon be strong enough to lift something? Let the children try putting a piece of card on the deflated balloon and then squeezing the bottle. What happens to the card? Why?

- Could air lift something heavier?

Teacher demonstration: Put an empty plastic carrier bag on the table with the opening overhanging the edge of the table. Place a pile of books on the bag, then gather up the opening of the bag into a small hole and blow slowly into it. What happens to the books? Try with more books and see what happens. The children can weigh the books and see what weight of books their teacher has lifted by blowing into the bag.

WARNING: It would not be safe for the children to do this experiment themselves.

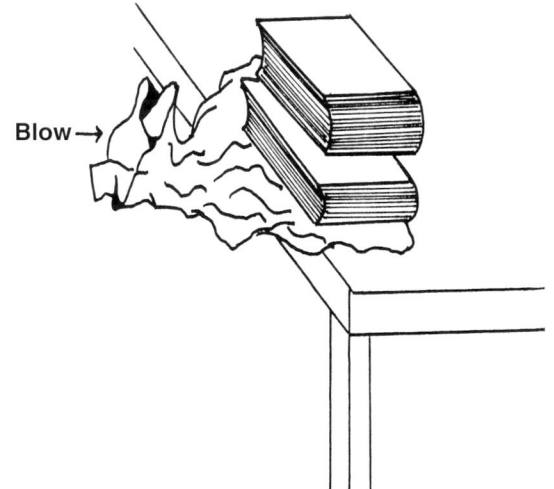

- Older children can also experiment with pneumatics using two syringes attached to each other with 3mm flexible plastic tubing.

WARNING: This is an ideal opportunity to warn children about not touching syringes in places other than in the classroom.

- Encourage the children to investigate the effect of using different sized syringes: 2ml, 5ml, 10ml, 20ml.

WARNING: Give the children goggles to wear and explain that they will have to be careful. A large syringe can push out a small syringe with great force.

- How will the children make Humpty Dumpty? Experiment layering with gummed tape. What happens if two layers are stuck together? Let them dry. Do they feel stronger than one layer?

- Try with three layers, four layers, five layers, etc. Let the children label how many layers their experimental pieces have, and compare them when they are dry. Is it easy to cut or bend a piece made from ten layers?

- Explain how they can build two or three layers of gummed tape over an inflated balloon and let it dry to get an egg shape. How will they cut the egg shape to make Humpty Dumpty break open? How will they decorate it?

ASSIGNMENTS
To design and make a falling Humpty Dumpty using pneumatic forces

Designing
- Let the children discuss and plan the model they are going to make. Ask them to make sketches of their designs.

- What materials will they make the wall from? Let them consider how they could build the wall from boxes. Investigate building walls using construction kits, etc.

- Will they add the king's horses and men to their models?

Making
- Let the children use small boxes to build the wall. How will they join the bricks together?

- How will they stop their wall falling over? Encourage them to consider using buttressing, or other methods of support (see examples in Teacher's Notes on page 38). Let them work together in groups, discussing and evaluating their designs as they proceed.

- Encourage them to try using different techniques to create textured effects on the boxes to resemble bricks (using, for example, sponge dabbed over wet paint, or by mixing sand with paint).

- The children can make their egg shape over the balloon using gummed tape. How many layers will they use? Once it is dry they can decide where they want the break to be, mark it with a pen, and cut it in half. With younger children, the first cut is best made by the teacher using pointed scissors, and the children can then continue using their own scissors.

- Have lots of collage materials available to dress Humpty Dumpty.

- Where will Humpty Dumpty sit? How will he sit on the wall? How will he fall off the wall? Will they use a balloon and bottle, or syringes, to make him fall?

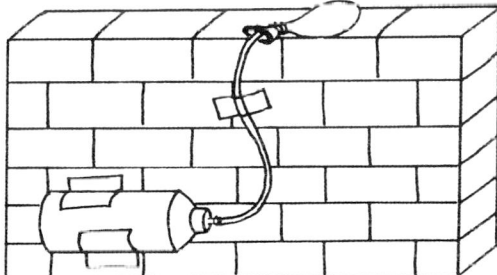

- Assemble the pneumatic mechanism and, once they are satisfied that it all works, the children can tape everything into position behind the wall.

EVALUATION
- Test the model. Does Humpty Dumpty fall off the wall? Does he break? Do you like the way your model works? Do you like the way your model looks? What did your audience think?

- Can you make Humpty Dumpty fall off the wall in time with the reciting of the nursery rhyme?

EXTENSION ACTIVITIES

- Investigate hydraulics.

- Pull the plunger to the top of an empty syringe, place your finger over the nozzle and push the plunger down. How far can you push it? What is in the syringe? Now fill the syringe with water and block the nozzle with your finger. Can you push the plunger down now?

- Find out more about hydraulics. Take two syringes and remove the plungers. Submerge the syringe components, together with a piece of flexible plastic tubing that fits the syringes, into a bowl of water. (The water can be coloured by adding a few drops of food dye to give a clearer effect). Under water, put the plunger back into the first syringe and compress fully. Join the tubing to this syringe, being careful to keep everything submerged. Then pull out the plunger to fill this syringe and tubing and, still keeping everything under water, attach the second syringe to the other end of the tubing. Take both syringes out of the water and let the children try to slowly push the plunger of one syringe. Is it easy to control? Does it move smoothly?

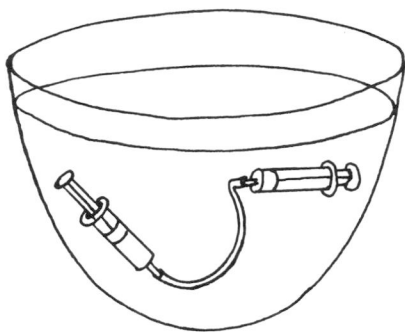

- Repeat this experiment using two air-filled syringes of the same size as above with the same length of tubing as above, and ask the same questions. Is this a fair test of the differences between pneumatics and hydraulics?

LANGUAGE OPPORTUNITIES

- Explore rhymes with predictable repetitive patterns, and explore rhyming strings, for example, *wall, fall, tall.*

- Children can write their own alternative rhymes for Humpty Dumpty.

Teacher's notes:
- The children can explore various methods of supporting their wall.

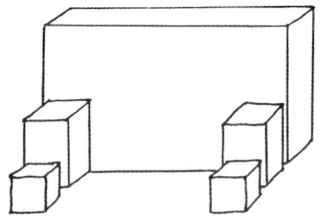

Small cereal boxes used as buttressing

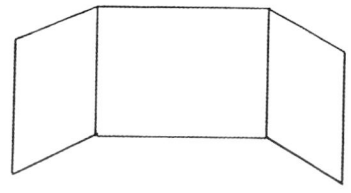

Folded card

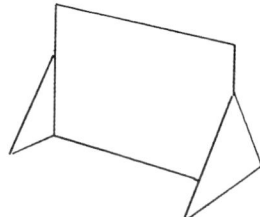

Triangular card as supports

- **Air power** (pneumatics) uses compressed air to transfer movement/power from one place to another.
- **Water power** (hydraulics) uses water to transfer movement/power from one place to another.

SPRINGS

Edmund
- I used thin wire to make my Spring,
- I rolled the wire around a tube,
- My box has Velcro to keep it closed,

Jamie
- I folded card to make my Spring.
- I used ribbon tied to my box to hold my Spring down.

Laura
- I folded my card
- My Spring looked like this
- I used a ribbon around my box to hold my Spring snake down,

Cedric
- I rolled wire around a rolling pin to make my Spring
- I used elastic and a toggle to keep my box closed

Clemency
- I used sponge for my Spring,
- The box is tied with elastic to hold the Spring down

AIM OF PROJECT: To design and make a Jack-in-the-box

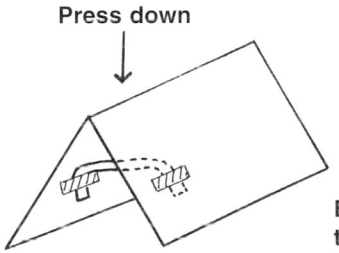

RESOURCES

Materials for making springs: stiff card, sponge, elastic bands, wire and tubes or dowels to wrap it around
Corrugated plastic
Strong, small boxes
Strong tape (for attaching springs)
Paper and glue for covering boxes
Rulers for measuring paper
Felt-tip pens to add details
A variety of collage materials, including textiles, polystyrene balls, etc.

STARTING POINTS

- Have a collection of Jack-in-the-box toys for the children to explore.
- Why does the toy pop up when the box is opened? What stops it from popping right out of the box?

INVESTIGATIONS

- Let the children experiment with taping an elastic band to both sides of a folded card. What happens?

Press down

Elastic band taped to both sides of the folded card

MOVING PICTURES

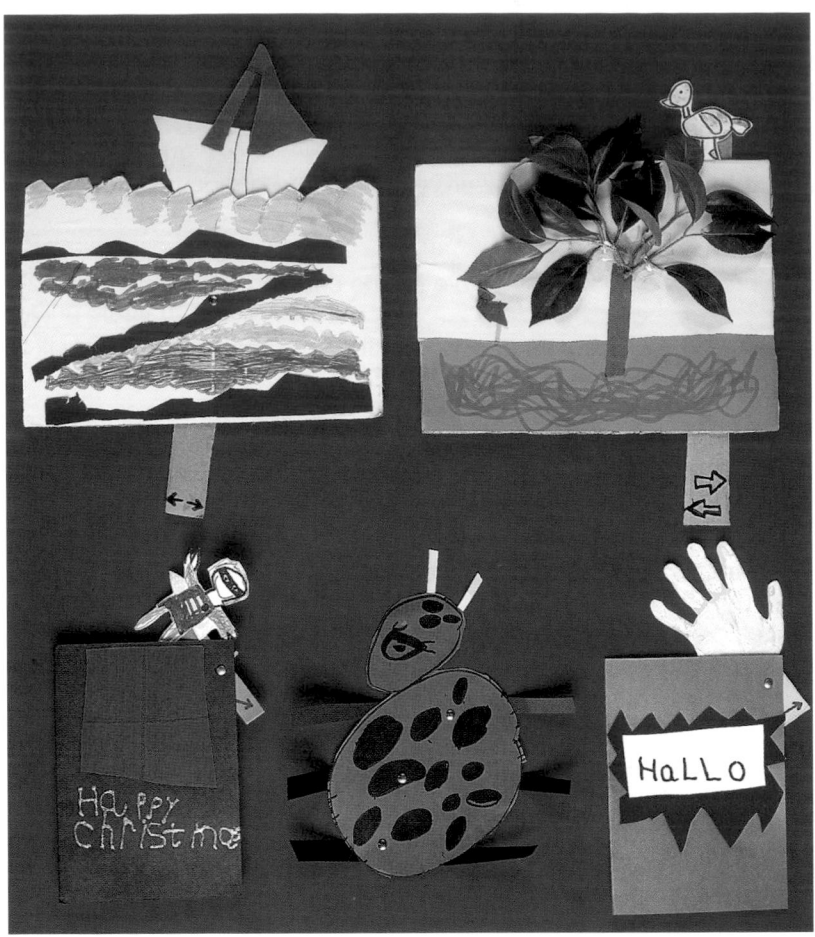

AIM OF PROJECT: To design and make a picture with moving parts

RESOURCES

A selection of pop-up books
Card
Split pins
A collection of empty tins with lids
Spoons of various sizes
Cardboard or balsa wood
Hole punches, paper drills

Nails
Small weights
Collage materials, felt-tip pens, paint
PVA glue, glue sticks
Rulers
Wooden blocks

STARTING POINTS

• Look at a variety of 'pop-up' books with tabs and levers for moving the pictures. Discuss how some of the mechanisms work by pushing and pulling the tabs.
• Attach a strip of card to a piece of cardboard using a split pin. Let the children handle this and explore how it is made. How does it work? What happens when one end is pushed or pulled? Does the other end move? Does it move in the same direction as the end that was pushed?

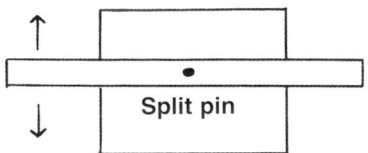

Split pin

INVESTIGATIONS

• Have a collection of clean and empty tins with lids that need to be levered off to open. How can the lids be taken off? Allow the children ample time to explore the possibilities. Why is the lid difficult to open using your fingers?

- Introduce spoons of various sizes. How could these help? Let them all try it out for themselves. Why does using the spoon make opening the tin easier?

- Does it make any difference if you push down at different points on the spoon (A, B, C)?

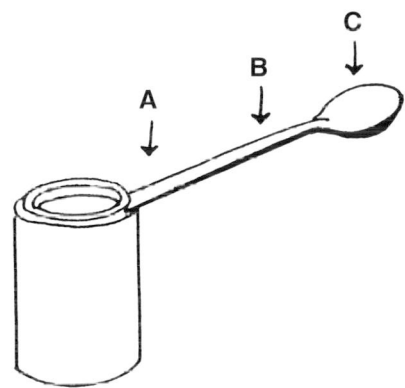

- Relate this to see-saws. Let the children use rulers and wooden blocks to explore how see-saws work. Introduce and explain the words: *fulcrum, pivot, effort, load.*

- Would the see-saw work differently if they used a square, round or triangular pivot?

- Encourage the children to make predictions and then try it for themselves to see what happens. Ask them to make labelled sketches.

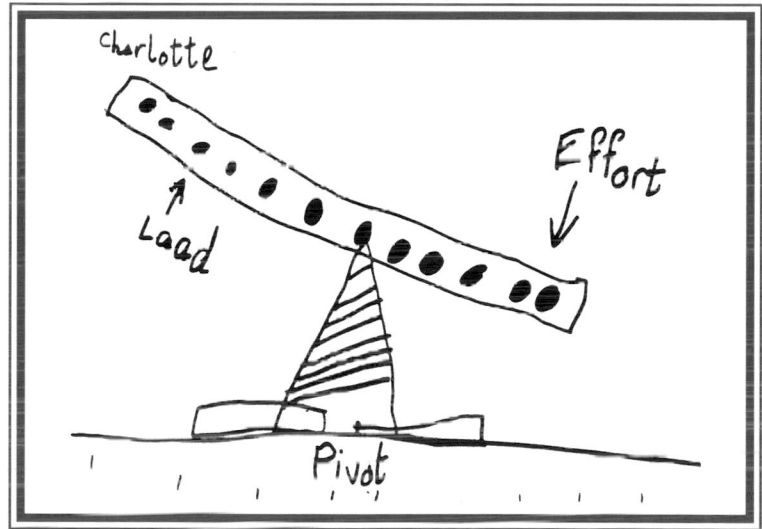

- What happens if you move the pivot point? Let the children predict and then try it out.

- Older children could measure the distance the load has moved as the pivot point changes. Give them time to investigate how the position of the pivot can alter the distance the load can move.

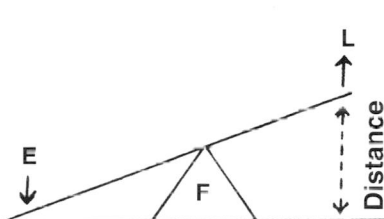

If the pivot/fulcrum is far from the effort, the load will move only a short distance, but you will find it easy to move the load up.

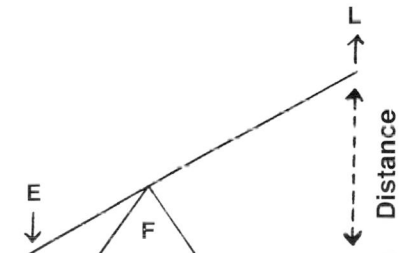

If the pivot/fulcrum is close to the effort, the load will move a much longer distance, but you will find it harder to move the load up.

L = Load   F = Fulcrum   E = Effort

- Can you make the see-saw balance with a weight on each end?

- Can you balance one weight on one end and three on the other end?

- Using a strip of cardboard or balsa wood, the children can make a see-saw scale. The pivot can be folded stiff card and the pivot point can be a nail pushed through a hole in the balsa wood strip and pivot.

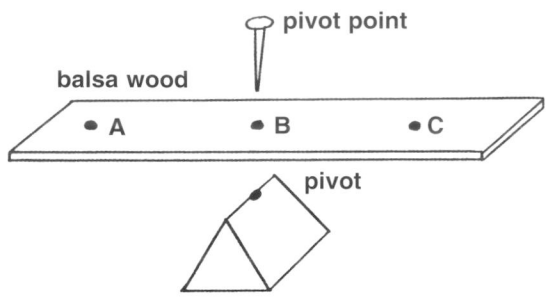

- The children can use this to make a challenge game, and invite another class to try and balance one 100g weight on one side of the scale against two 100g weights on the other.

- Older children can also try to predict the distance the load will move upwards if the pivot point is moved, for example, to points A, B and C on the illustration shown above.

ASSIGNMENTS
To design and make a picture with moving parts

Designing
- Explain to the children that they are going to design and make a picture that has a moving part. Show them the card you used in the starting points and let them attach a drawing on one end and move the other end. Note what happens to the drawing.

- Brainstorm other ways they could use a moving lever in their pictures. Will their lever show on the front of the picture or be hidden on the back? What will their pictures be of? Which part will move? What materials will they use for decoration: collage, felt-tip pens, paint?

- Encourage the children to explore different ways that they could make their levers work and how they could use levers to move different parts of the picture.

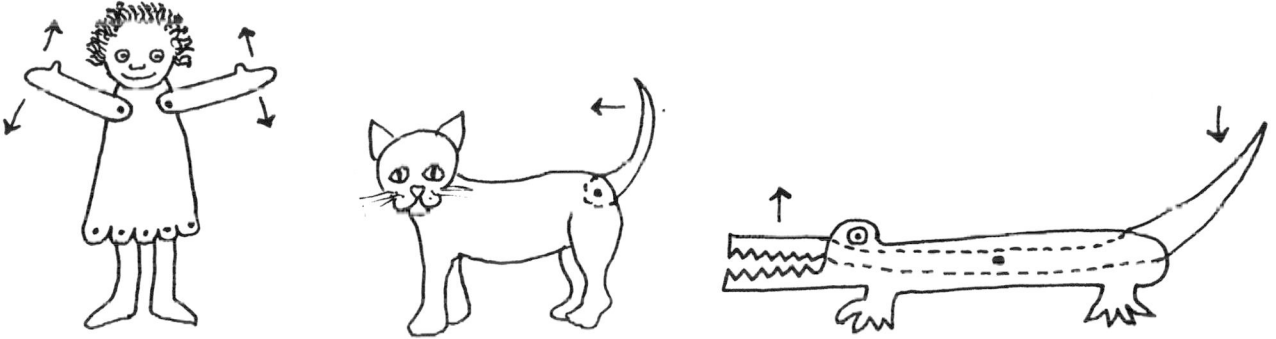

- Ask the children to make sketches of their ideas. Let them decide the size of their picture.

- Using scrap card, the children can make mock-ups of how their levers will work.

- Show the children how to use a split pin to join the two holes.

Making
- Encourage the children to plan the order in which they will make their pictures. Remind them that if they are using paint, they will have to wait for it to dry before attaching their levers.

- Have a large variety of collage materials available so that the children can experiment with lots of different finishes in making their picture. Encourage them to try and create 3D effects with crumpled tissue paper, fabric, leaves, etc.

- Encourage the children to refer to their design sketches and ideas as they proceed.

- Attach the lever to the picture by punching a hole into the lever and using a paper drill to make a hole in their picture. Explain that the lever should be attached after their picture has been decorated.

- Encourage the children to evaluate as they proceed. For example, if their levers are too long and floppy, they can use thicker card for the lever. If the lever moves too much, they can use a tab to restrict the movement.

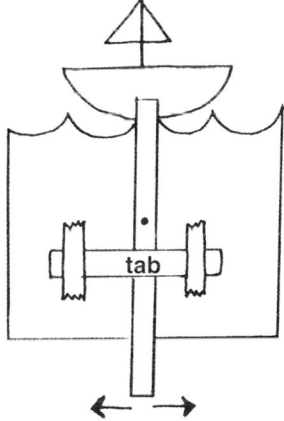

EVALUATION
- Test your picture. Does the lever on your moving picture work? Is the effect good, or would you change or improve it if you made it again?

- Would someone else trying to move the lever know which way to push or pull it? How could you make this clear?

EXTENSION ACTIVITIES

- Can the children make a series of moving pictures to compile a 'pop-up' type book?

- Look at linkages. Make cards or pictures based on linkages. (A linkage is a means of connecting components, such as levers, so that they can produce a particular movement.)

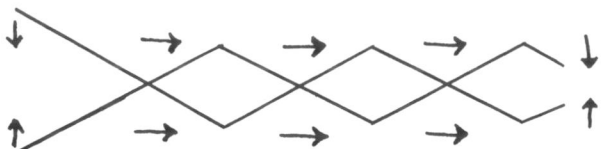

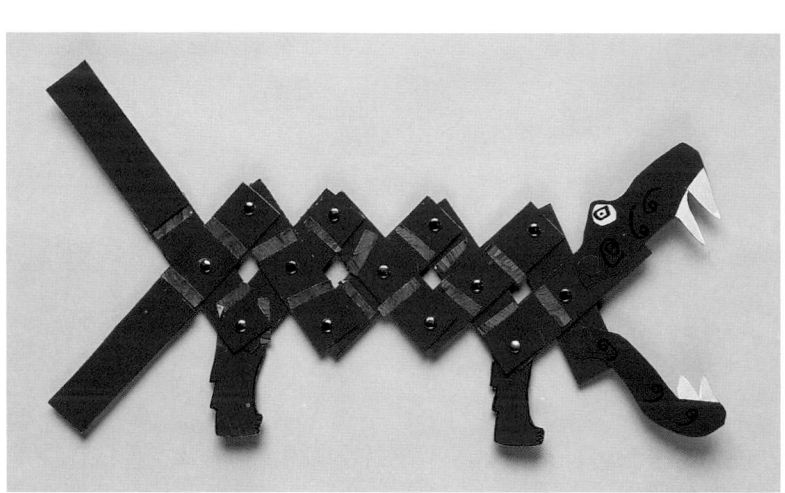

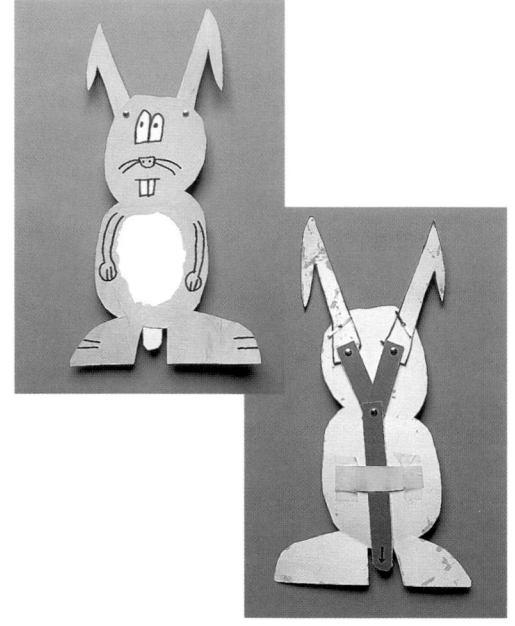

LANGUAGE OPPORTUNITIES

- Write a story using your picture as a stimulus. This could be compiled into a 'pop-up' book if several moving pictures are developed.

- Write out a series of instructions for the challenge game (see page 44).

Teacher's notes: In this project, the children will explore 1st class levers. The other two types are 2nd and 3rd class. (See illustrations below.)

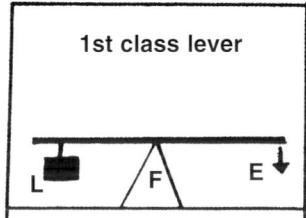

1st class lever

The fulcrum is between the load and the effort, e.g. a see-saw.

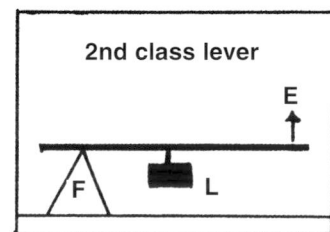

2nd class lever

The load is between the effort and the fulcrum, e.g. a wheel-barrow.

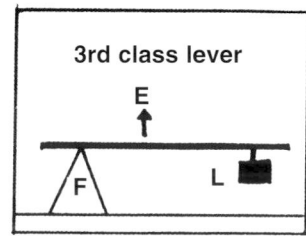

3rd class lever

The effort is between the load and the fulcrum, e.g. a fishing rod.

L = Load   **F** = Fulcrum   **E** = Effort

AIM OF PROJECT: To design and make a shadow puppet

RESOURCES

Pictures/books about shadow puppets
Coloured card, black and white card
Cooking oil, brushes and paper towels
Acetate sheet or Cellophane in different colours
Hole punches, paper drills and staplers
Adhesive tape and masking tape

Split pins
Material for screen, e.g. white cotton sheeting or
a large sheet of tracing paper
Woodstrip, thin dowel and saws
Glue, drawing pins, scissors
Felt-tip pens

STARTING POINTS

- Look at pictures and books about shadow puppets. Find out about Chinese, Javanese and Turkish shadow puppets.
- What is a shadow puppet? How are they put together? How do they move?

INVESTIGATIONS

- Begin by looking at shadows. What is a shadow? How is it formed? Where have you seen shadows? Can you make shadow creatures with your hands?

- Put up a piece of white cloth to use as a screen, with a light source behind it, and let the children experiment with making shadows using their hands. Try different light sources: a well-lit window, an overhead projector, an anglepoise lamp. Explore which light source makes the best shadow.

- Investigate the best position for the puppet screen and light source to achieve the best shadow using card. What happens to the shadow if the card is closer to the light source?

- Make shadows using pieces of coloured card as well as white card coloured with felt-tip pens. Does it make any difference to the colour of the shadow if the card is coloured? What happens to the shadows if you punch holes into the card?

- Give the children a small quantity of oil in a small container and remind them that a little goes a long way! Let the children rub oil over the coloured card. Show them how to apply oil sparingly on both sides of the card and rub off the excess with paper towels. What happens? Hold the oiled card up to the light. Can you see through the card? Hold it up behind the lit screen. Can you see colour now? Why?

- Try holding acetate sheets or Cellophane behind the screen. What happens? Introduce the words *opaque, translucent, transparent*.

- Can the children make a chart or display board to explain their findings?

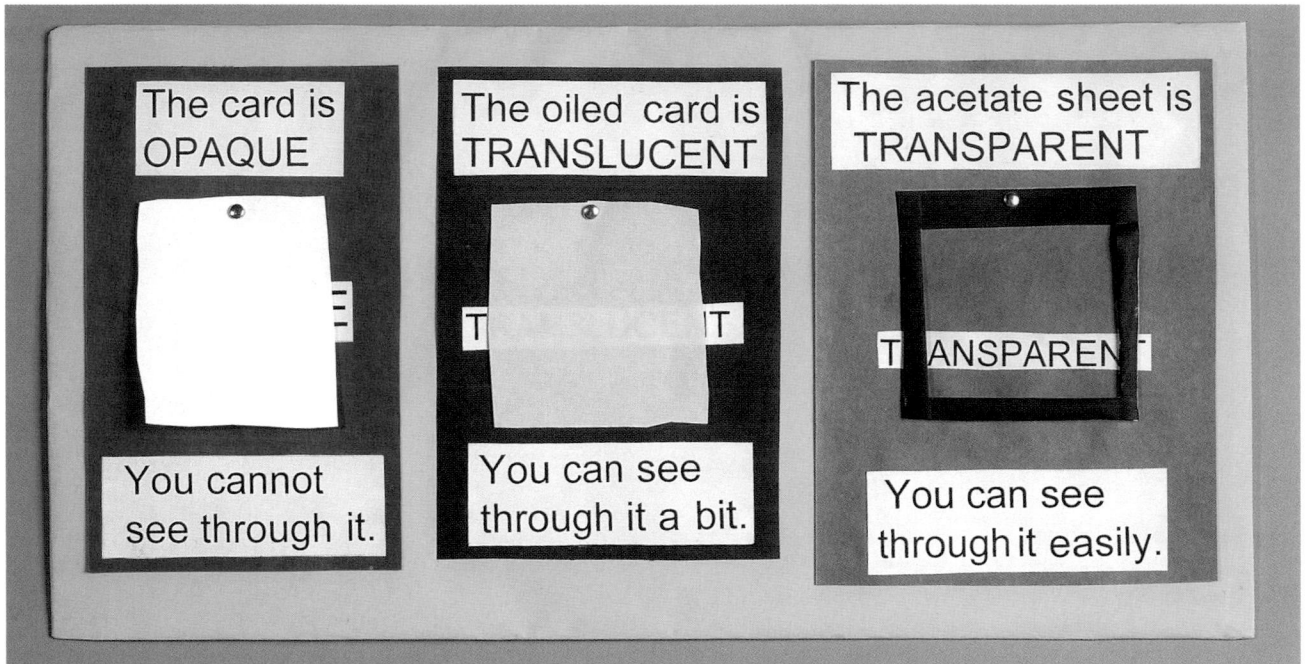

ASSIGNMENTS
To design and make a shadow puppet

Designing
- Ask the children to consider the size that their screen will be. How will they make it? They could use woodstrip and card triangles to make a frame and cover this with white cloth, or have a cloth hung from a line.

- How will the cloth be attached to the screen: drawing pins? masking tape?

- Using construction kits, the children can design and investigate ways of making their screen stand up (see facing page).

- Brainstorm ideas for the kind of puppets the children want to make. Can the children think of ways to make a puppet move? Perhaps investigate traditional puppets with moving parts. Remind the children to consider the size of their puppet in relation to the screen. Ask them to sketch their ideas and consider the materials and decoration to be used.

- Have card, hole punches, paper drills and split pins available for the children to experiment with, making holes in the card and joining two pieces of card together with a split pin. Give them time to explore and discover the need for the two pieces of card to overlap. Do the pieces of card move? Why?

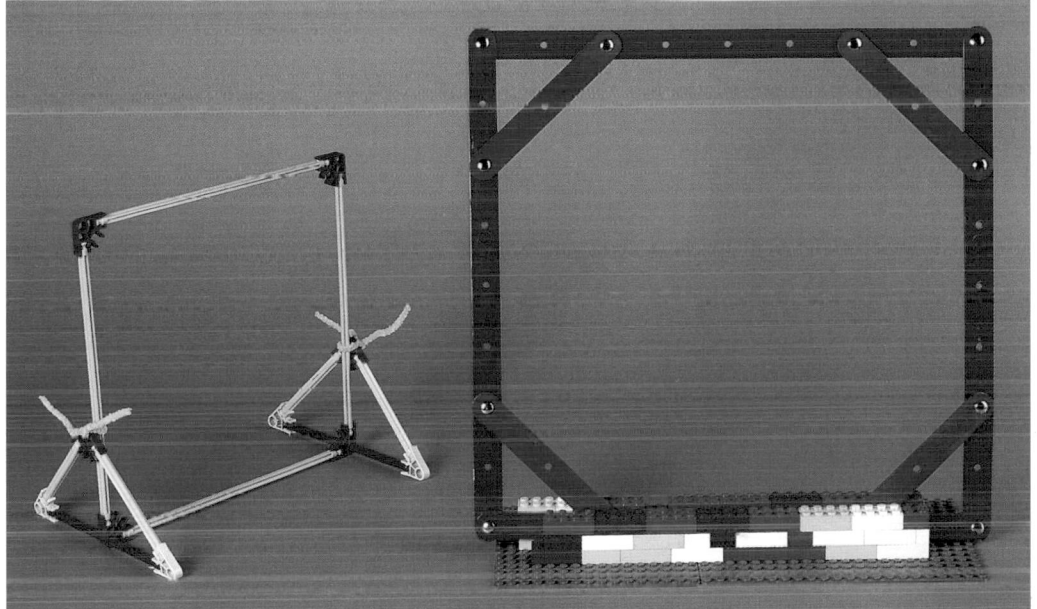

Designs for a screen

- What happens if there are two split pins? Do the pieces of card move now? Why not?

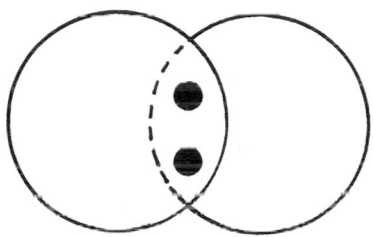

- Ask questions to enable the children to develop their understanding about how to create moving joints.

- Encourage them to sketch a design showing the overlap and positions of split pins and support sticks.

This sketch was done after researching iguanas.

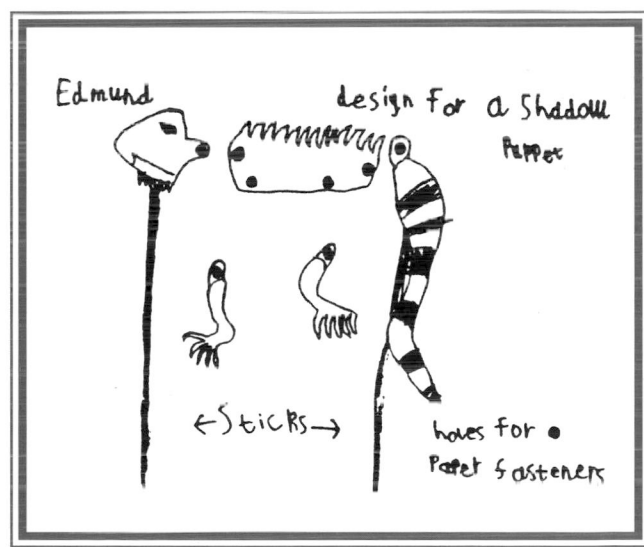

This design was made using the sketch and considering where the joints would go, and how they would overlap.

Making

- Have a selection of materials and tools available for the children to choose from. Discuss which they will need to make their design. Ask them to think about the order in which they will make their puppets. Will they oil their card before or after they have decorated the puppet with felt-tip pens? Will they make the holes for the split pins before or after cutting out their puppets?

- Draw puppet design on card and cut out. Encourage the children to be economical in their use of card sheets. Should they cut into the middle of the sheet?

- Let the children decorate their puppets using felt-tip pens. Once satisfied, they can apply oil sparingly to both sides. Let this dry overnight and then put in the split pins.

- Explain how to hold dowel in a vice prior to sawing in order to make support sticks.

- Decide where to attach the support sticks (i.e. where the puppet balances best and gives good movement). Try various positions (using a temporary fixing, for example, masking tape) to see how gravity and balance affect the way the puppet moves.

- How can the stick be attached permanently to the puppet? (For this project the children used strong tape and staplers.)

- Make the screen, keeping in mind your design decisions (see Introduction for use of woodstrip and card triangles for creating a strong structure for the screen).

EVALUATION

- Test the shadow puppet.

- Discuss the strengths and weaknesses of the puppets. Do they move well?

- How well does the screen work? Is the structure stable?

EXTENSION ACTIVITIES

- Investigate punching holes all over card. How does this affect the shadows?

- Set up a projector so that the light will fall on a wall. Tape a large piece of paper to the wall. Let children take it in turns to sit in profile between the projector beam and the wall. Explain why they must not look directly at the beam. The outline of the silhouette can be drawn onto the paper. Does the silhouette change if the children move closer to, or further from, the beam?

LANGUAGE OPPORTUNITIES

- Write a character study of your puppet. How might it behave? What would it sound like? What would it say?

- In a group, write a play script for your puppets. Think about the intended audience. Perform the play.

- Make posters to advertise the puppet show.

- Write a programme for the puppet show.

- Explore shadow writing using the computer.

Teacher's notes:
- Shadows are formed when an object (e.g. the puppet) blocks off part of the light source.

- The distance that the puppet is held from the screen determines the clarity of the image. Held close to the screen, the image is crisp and clear; the further away from the screen the puppet is, the more diffused the image.

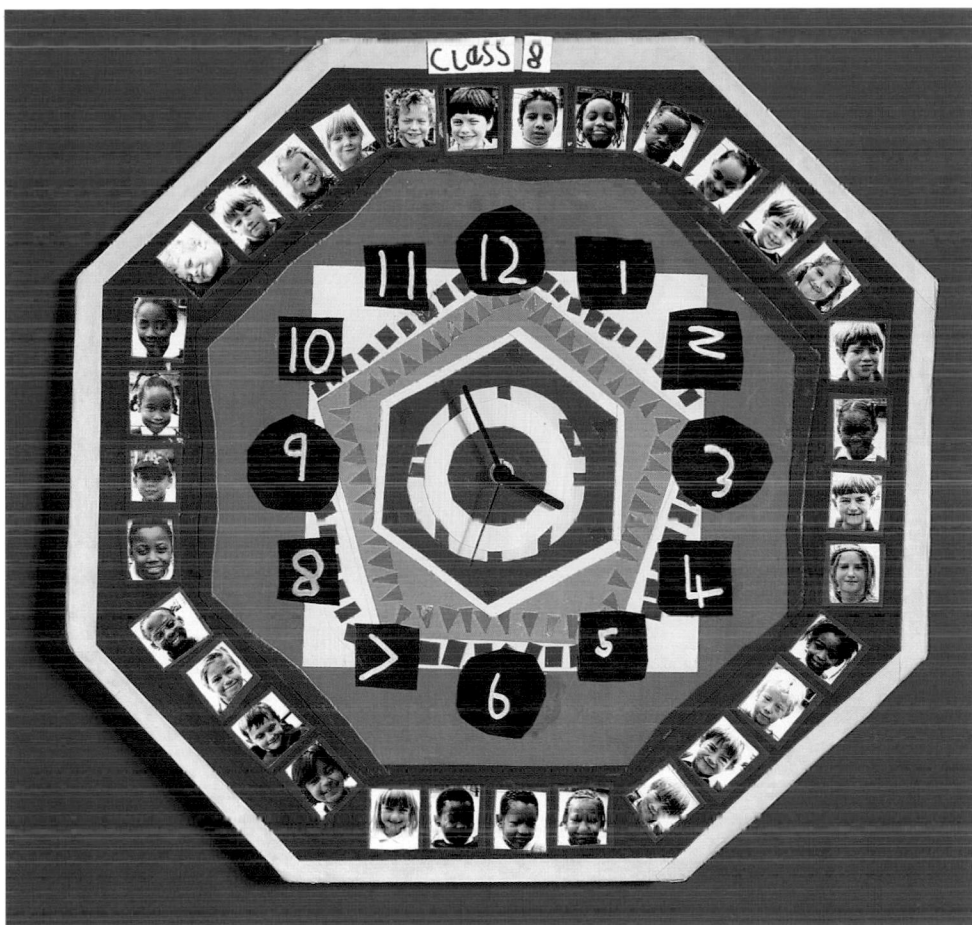

AIM OF PROJECT: To design and make a classroom clock

RESOURCES
Round wooden board, about 30cm diameter, with a hole in the middle
(**Note:** you might need a larger board as the shadows can be very long, depending on the time of year and locality)
Short length of wooden dowel or a pencil that fits snugly into the hole on the board
Ruler and permanent marker
Clock mechanism and one AA battery cell to operate it
Clock hands
Templates of shapes in different sizes
Paper drill to make hole in centre of clock for clock mechanism
Thin card in various colours

STARTING POINTS
- Ask the children to estimate the time of day without looking at their watch or clocks. How do they know what time of day it is? What points of reference do they use to help them?
- How did people tell the time before there were clocks? Discuss ideas.
- Talk about how sand clocks, water clocks and candle clocks were used to tell the time.
- Consider how the position of the sun in the sky can help to judge the time of day.
- Talk about the sun casting shadows. Do these shadows stay the same all day? Do they change position? Do they change length?
- Let the children go outside and draw the outline of each other's shadows in chalk on the playground. What happens when they stand in the same place later In the day? Are the shadows in the same position? Are they the same length?
- Could the fact that shadows change their length and position during the day be used for telling the time?

WARNING: Remind the children that they must never look directly at the sun.

INVESTIGATIONS

- Investigate making a shadow clock. Provide the children with a round wooden board with a hole in its centre and a pencil or short length of dowelling to fit into the hole tightly. Let them fit the dowel into the hole vertically, at 90° angle.

- Explain that the board, which will have the shadow markings on it, is called the *plate*, and the dowel, which will cast the shadow, is called the *gnomon*.

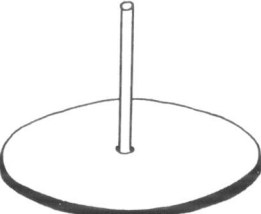

- Let the children explore the playground and choose a suitable level position where they think shadows will be cast by the sun and where their shadow clock will not be disturbed. Help them to set their shadow clock into position, making sure that it is level, secure and cannot move.

- The children can mark the position of the sun once every hour during the day using a ruler and permanent marker.

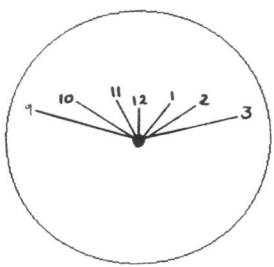

- Let the children measure the length of each of the shadows created by the gnomon, and then make a graph or line chart to record the results.

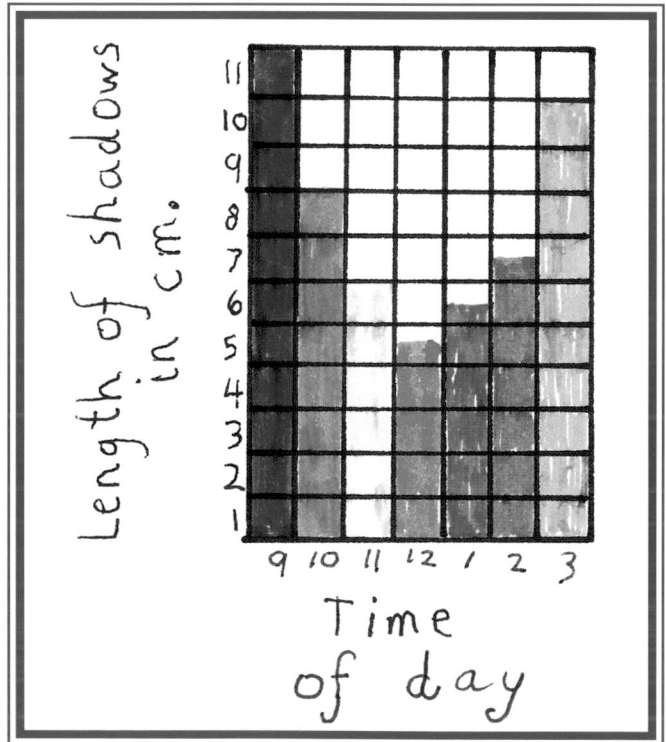

- Did the shadow change position during the day? Did the length of the shadow change during the day?

- At what time was the shadow the shortest? At what time was the shadow the longest? At what time of the day do you think that the Earth was furthest from the Sun?

- Ask the children why their shadow clocks do not go all the way round in a circle like their wrist watches? Could they use their shadow clock to tell the time at night, or on a cloudy day? How accurate is their shadow clock at telling the time? Explain that their shadow clock will only tell the local time.

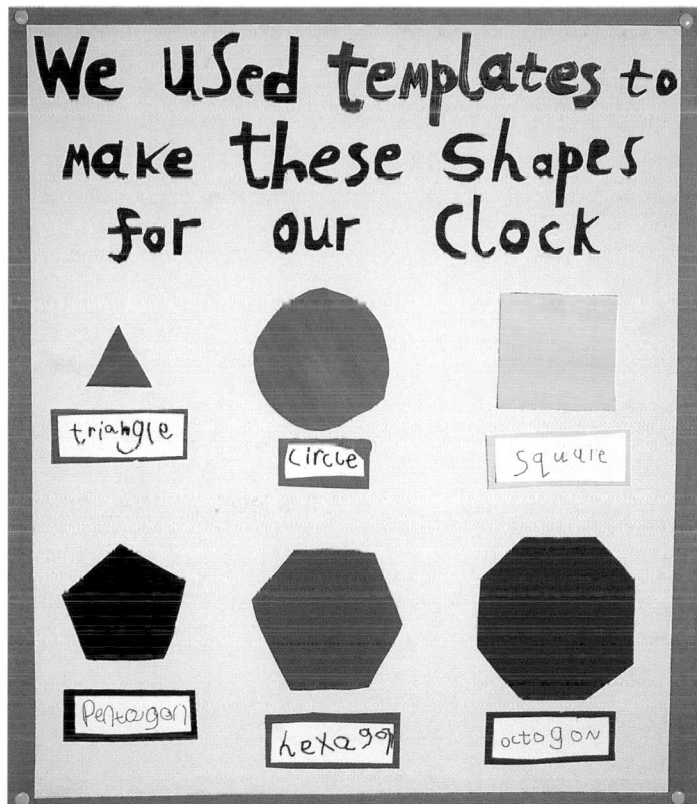

ASSIGNMENTS
To design and make a classroom clock

Designing

- Discuss the need to tell the time more accurately than with shadows. How do we do this?

- Let the children look at clocks and pictures of clocks. What designs of clock do they like best? Are the numbers always in the same place? Why?

- Encourage the children to design a clock for the classroom. Let them discuss what they would like their class clock to look like. How big will it be? What shape will it be? What colours will it be? Let them discuss and work out their design together in teams. Ask them to sketch their designs.

- Explain to the children that they will be using a battery operated clock mechanism to operate the clock that they are going to design and make. Show them the mechanism and explain that the spindle goes through the clock face and that the hands are attached on the front.

Making

- This is a good opportunity for children to work together as a team. Let them brainstorm the size and shape that they want their clock to be. Remind them to consider that they will need a hole in the centre of the clock face. How many layers of card will their clock have? Let them measure their spindle and explain that their clock face must not be thicker than the spindle.

  NOTE: Each group of children who created the clock face on page 51 chose a geometrical shape and made one layer of the clock face. They glued the shapes together in descending size so that each layer showed. They then chose to decorate the completed clock face with small geometrical shapes.

- Where are they going to put the numbers? Explain how to divide the face into quarters in order to place the 12, 3, 6 and 9. The remaining numbers could be placed by measuring the distance between the quarters using standard or non-standard measurements (for example, a ruler or using finger widths). Encourage the children to stand back and view their clock from a distance.

  NOTE: In this project, the placing of the numbers took great care and concentration - it was a real group effort. Once the clock was finished, the children decided that they wanted to make it more personal to their class. They decided to have photographs of themselves all around the clock. They took photos of each other in pairs, and then cut them out and glued them around the clock.

- Make the hole in the centre of the clock face using a paper drill. Attach the mechanism as shown in the illustration.

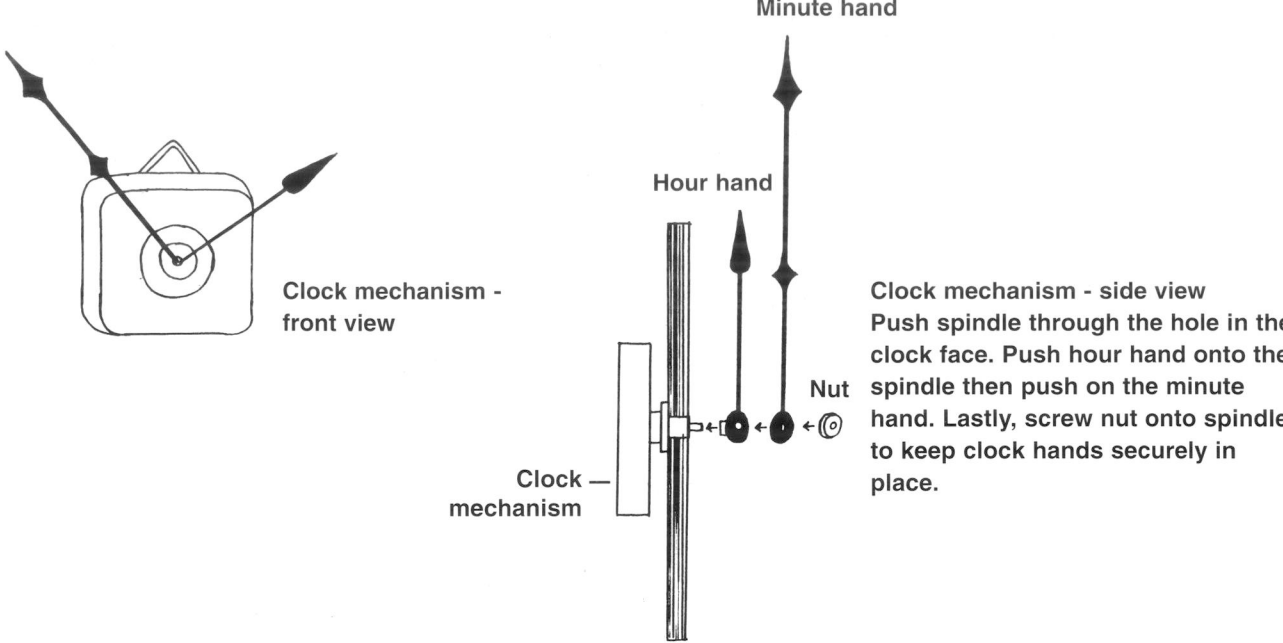

Minute hand

Hour hand

Clock mechanism - front view

Clock — mechanism

Nut

Clock mechanism - side view
Push spindle through the hole in the clock face. Push hour hand onto the spindle then push on the minute hand. Lastly, screw nut onto spindle to keep clock hands securely in place.

- Gently turn the clock hands to show the correct time and put a battery into the mechanism. Over the following days, let the children check whether their clock keeps accurate time.

- Consider how the clock will be hung (for example, using string and tape).

EVALUATION
- Test your clock. Does it work? Can you tell the time on your clock? Can you read the numbers? Are they clear? Will other people be able to read them?

- What do you think of your clock? What changes/improvements would you make?

EXTENSION ACTIVITIES
- Explore time in general - for example, learning to tell the time and relating this to days, weeks, months, years and the seasons.

- Having studied the months and seasons, the children could make a calendar for their classroom (see page 1).

LANGUAGE OPPORTUNITIES
- Keep individual diaries or a class diary to record school events over a period of time.

- Keep a time log for a day in their life.

- Talk about the use of different tenses and their relevant word endings, for example, *ed, ing,* to show the passing of time.

Teacher's notes:
The sun reaches its highest point at midday, when it crosses the meridian (a.m. stands for ante-meridian, p.m. for post-meridian). The shadow will therefore be shortest at midday (the higher the sun, the shorter the shadow) and point due north.

DESIGNER WEAR

AIM OF PROJECT: To design and make a motif for a T-shirt

RESOURCES

White cotton T-shirts (ask parents to supply them or the children could just use small pieces of white cotton)
Fabric glue for fixing a photocopy face down onto fabric (if not available, use transfer fabric paints which are
   painted onto paper and then ironed face down onto fabric)
Scraps of cloth on which to experiment
Collage materials, paint, brushes and paper
Rolling pins, card to put inside the T-shirts, to prevent the back and front from sticking together
Aprons, newspaper to cover surfaces
Identical plastic bottles, pieces of textiles and thermometers
Paints, felt-tip pens
Hand lenses
Mirrors
Sponge
Access to photocopier

STARTING POINTS

• Ask the children to bring in, or wear, their favourite T-shirts. Talk about them and discuss why they like
  them. Look at the labels and find out what fabric their T-shirts are made from.

• Look at a plain T-shirt. How could you get a picture onto it? Could you use paint? What would happen if
  you washed it?

INVESTIGATIONS

• Let the children paint a scrap of cloth and put it into water. Why does the paint wash off? Why does this
  not happen to their T-shirts?

- Have a variety of cotton textile scraps for the children to examine. Let them use hand lenses to observe the weave, and sort them into woven and knitted samples. Encourage them to sketch what they observe.

- Does cotton keep us warmer or cooler than other fabrics? Encourage the children to devise a fair test to find out.

- This could be investigated by filling identical plastic bottles with the same amount of water at a temperature of 40°C and wrapping a different material around each bottle, for example, wool, PVC, cotton, foil, fur, etc. Predict which bottle will lose/retain most heat. Take the temperature of the water in each bottle after 45 minutes to assess the heat loss. Which material allowed the most heat to escape? Which material kept the bottle warm? Which material would you prefer to wear on a hot day? Why? Which material would it be best to wear on a cold day? Why? Ensure that your test was fair and that only one factor changed.

- What is cotton? Find out about cotton using the library or CD-Rom to research information about what it needs to grow, where it grows, what the life cycle of the cotton plant is, how long it takes from planting to harvesting, which part of the plant is used to make cotton, and how it is made into cotton. The children can also write to organisations such as The Textile Institute for small samples of raw cotton.

- The children can design and make a resource board of their discoveries (see facing page). Let them assemble and rearrange their information before securing its position. Encourage them to think about how to convey the information to their audience (other children, teachers and parents). Advise them to stand back and view their work from a distance as they proceed.

Mirror image
- Ask the children to look into the mirror and cover their right eye with their hand. Which eye is covered in the mirror image?

- Let them write their names on a piece of paper and look at the writing in the mirror. What happens?

- Discuss mirror images (with a view to preparing the children for reversing any writing on their T-shirt designs).

See Investigations on facing page

ASSIGNMENTS
To design and make a motif for a T-shirt

Designing

- Encourage the children to look at their T-shirts and decide where they want the design to be. What size will it be? What will their picture be of? Will they use paint, collage, pens, or computer? Do they want colour, or black and white?

- Encourage the children to sketch their design. Remind them that their writing should be reversed because of the mirror image (check using a mirror).

- Explain to the children that they are not going to paint directly onto the T-shirts because fabric creases and therefore needs to be stretched over a frame to give a suitable painting surface.

- They will design their picture on paper or computer, then photocopy it, and stick the photocopy face down onto their T-shirt. When the glue has dried they will be able to rub off the paper to reveal their design. If using fabric paints which need to be ironed on, make sure that the design is face down before it is ironed.

- Point out that because they will be using a photocopy, they can make as many copies as they like, all exactly the same. Consider designing and making a school T-shirt, perhaps for a special occasion, for example, a sports day, 50th Anniversary of the school, etc.

Making

- Once the children's designs are ready, demonstrate to them how to use the photocopier to reduce or enlarge their pictures.

- Show the children the fabric glue and explain that this is a glue that will stick a photocopy onto a fabric, so that they can paint, draw or make a collage of their design on paper, and then photocopy it and stick it onto their T-shirt.

- Explain that the front of their photocopy is glued face down onto the T-shirt, which means that their T-shirt will have a mirror image of their design. (If using paints, the design is ironed on face down and will also produce a mirror image.)

- When gluing the design onto the T-shirt, show the children how to put a piece of card inside the T-shirt to prevent the glue penetrating to the back of the T-shirt. Remind the children that they must apply the glue to the front of their photocopied picture.

- Children should be shown how to spread the glue evenly with a brush, working quickly so that the glue does not dry out, and making sure that the edges of the photocopy are well covered with glue.

- Position the photocopy onto the T-shirt and use a rolling-pin to roll the photocopy firmly down (onto the T-shirt).

- When the glue has dried (overnight), the paper can be rubbed off. Show the children how to wet the paper with a sponge and then use their fingers to rub the paper gently off. This will take a while to complete, so allow them plenty of time to do this slowly and carefully. It is a messy process with lots of small, damp pieces of paper about, so encourage them to cover surfaces (and floor) before they begin.

EVALUATION

How do your T-shirts look? Do you like them? Would you buy them if you saw them in a shop?

EXTENSION ACTIVITY

- Explore other mirror images, for example, kaleidoscopes. Hold two plastic mirrors at right angles to each other, and move them across the surface of patterned paper. Observe the images created.

LANGUAGE OPPORTUNITIES

- Encourage the children to find out about cotton from reference books. Point out that this is non-fiction and that they do not have to read the whole book. Explain about the use of the Contents and Index page.

- Ask the children to write advertising slogans to promote the sale of their T-shirts. Explore and develop the use of persuasive language to make their product desirable.

Teacher's notes:
If coloured images are designed, access to a colour photocopier is required.

PAPER AND PASTE

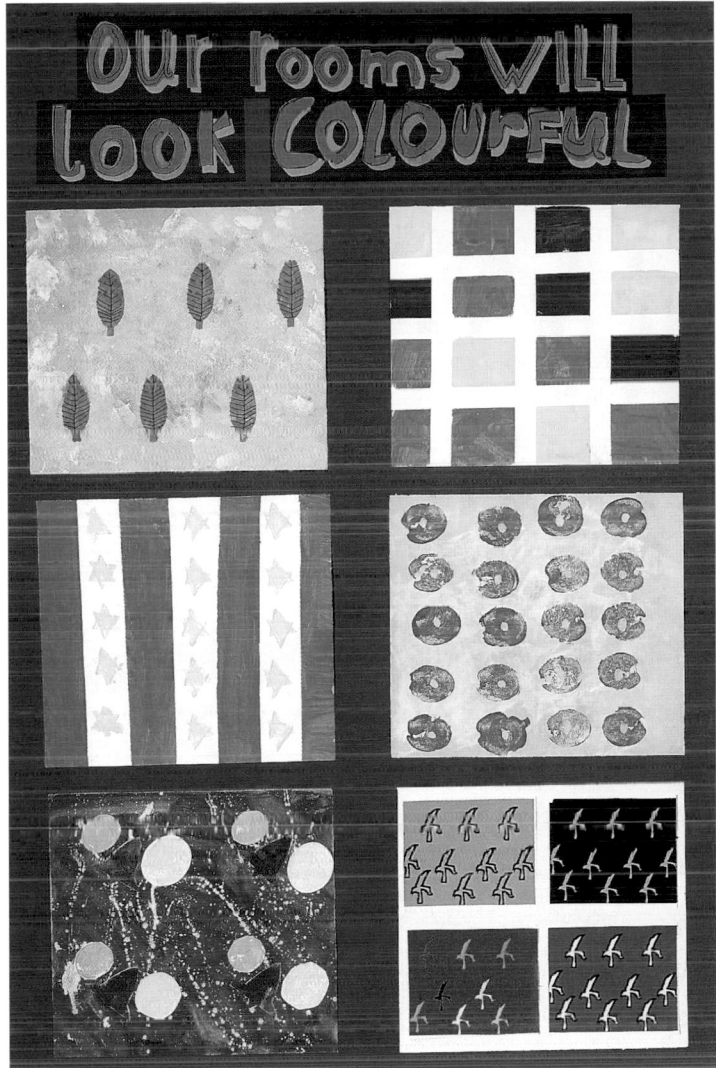

AIM OF PROJECT: To design and make wallpaper and paste

RESOURCES
Milk, lemons, vinegar, flour, dried egg white, gelatine
Sieve
Bucket with removable handle or scale pan, broom handle
500g bags of flour/sugar, etc.
Wallpaper pattern books (can often be obtained from DIY shops)
Sheets of paper, card, masking tape, scissors, paint, brushes, sponges, potatoes
Blunt knives (to cut potatoes with)
Large sheets of cardboard or hardboard to which the children can glue their wallpaper
A4 paper
Tablespoons/teaspoons
Clothes pegs
Beanbags, box, cushions

STARTING POINTS
- What is wallpaper? Why do we put it on our walls? What is it made of? Where does it come from? Where do the designs come from? How is it made?
- Collect samples and off-cuts of wallpaper from home or from wallpaper pattern books. Look at different colours, patterns and designs. Discuss which rooms and people they might be designed for. Encourage the children to explore their own personal preferences.
- How is wallpaper attached to the wall?

INVESTIGATIONS

- Investigate and make different types of wallpaper paste in the following way:

Flour paste glue: Mix one tablespoon of flour with two tablespoons of water.

Gelatine glue: Pour two tablespoons of warm water into a small container, sprinkle over one teaspoon of gelatine and stir. Continue stirring until the gelatine dissolves.

Egg white glue: Mix one teaspoon of dried egg white with one tablespoon of water.

Casein glue: Pour one tablespoon of warm milk into a small container. Add one teaspoon of acid (lemon juice or vinegar) and stir. When the curds separate from the whey, sieve. The curds are casein glue.

- How can the strength of each glue be tested? Devise a test to investigate the strength of each glue. Cut A4 paper into strips of 1cm wide. Glue can be applied to 1cm on the end and the strip stuck together with an overlap join.

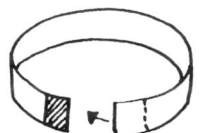

- Leave the glue to dry (about half an hour). Explain to the children that they can use a clothes peg or bulldog clip to hold the join in place until it dries.

- Hang the paper loop and a plastic bucket as shown in the sketch.

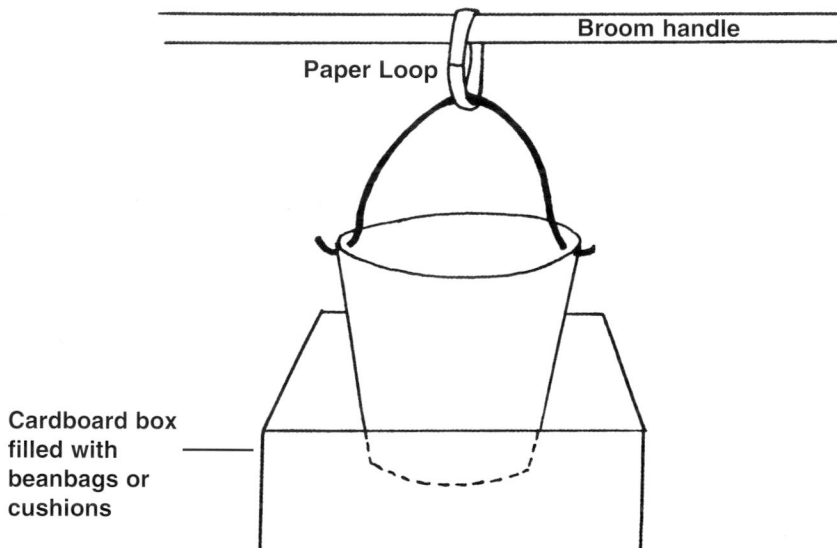

- When conducting this test, the children should be encouraged to consider the position of the join in the loop. Should it be positioned in the same place every time?

- The broom handle can be balanced between two tables, or two children can hold either end of the broom handle. The children then very carefully put 500g bags of flour or sugar into the bucket, one at a time until the loop breaks. How many 500g bags of flour or sugar did your paper loop hold before the bucket fell?

WARNING: Keep the gap between the floor and the bottom of the bucket as small as possible. The bucket will fall with a crash as the paper breaks because the paper loop can support a surprisingly large mass. A cardboard box filled with beanbags or small cushions should be placed under the bucket to cushion the fall.

- Did the loop break at the join, or did the paper break? Is your glue stronger than the paper?

- Encourage the children to compare the results of the tests on the different glues, and record their findings. Was this a fair test? Was the area which was covered the same for all the glues? Was the drying time the same? Was the paper the same?

- Forces are measured in newtons. Can you work out how many newtons your paper loop held? (Five newtons is the pull of gravity on a mass of 500g.) Use a newton metre to measure the force needed to break each loop.

ASSIGNMENTS
To design and make wallpaper and paste

Designing
- Let the children look through wallpaper pattern books to see as many examples of wallpaper patterns as they can. Encourage them to notice what colours are used and also what combination of colours are used together. Which papers do they like best?

- Let them sketch their own ideas and evaluate them as they proceed. Encourage them to ask themselves questions about their designs. What colours go well together? Are the patterns the right size? Which room is the paper for? Does the design look too 'busy' for a whole room?

- Notice how some wallpapers have a repeat pattern. How can the children make repeat patterns?

- Show the children how to cut a potato or sponge into the desired shape to make a design with a repeat pattern.

- How will they place their shape evenly? Will they fold the paper to mark it out? Will they measure the paper? Will they use masking tape as a temporary marking (for example, as a guide to painting straight lines)?

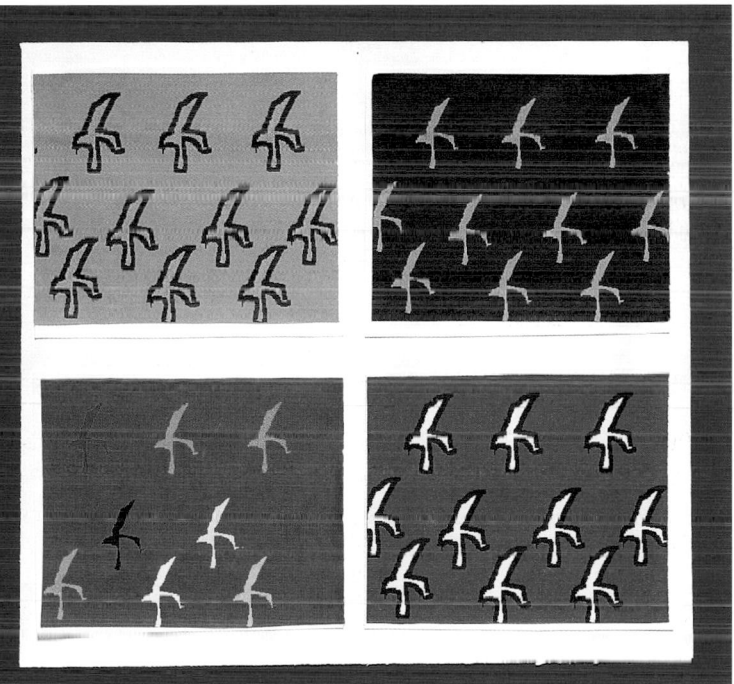

- Create designs on the computer and use the *Copy* and *Paste* facility to repeat the pattern. Learn how to change the colours to create different colourways.

- Show the children how to fold and cut thin card to make a stencil, and how to use masking tape to hold it securely while dabbing paint through it.
- Explain how to get pastel shades by adding white to paints of varying colours or by painting thinned-down white paint over dry coloured paint. Let the children experiment with this.
- Show them how to use a sponge to make a sponged or dappled effect.

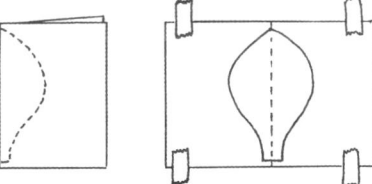

- The children can make a display board to show all this information.

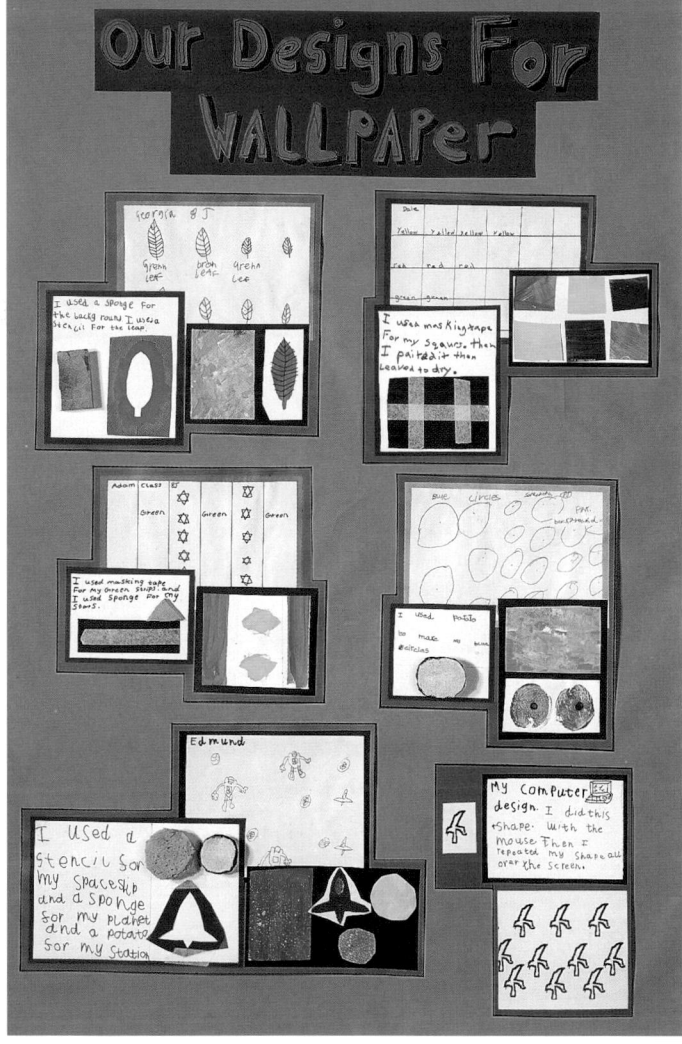

Making

- Explain to the children that it is important for them to plan the sequence in which they will make their sheet of wallpaper. For example, if using paint, the background colour will need time to dry before the patterns can be printed or painted onto it.
- Organise working areas. Do the children need to cover (with newspaper) the area on which they will be painting? Do they need to wear aprons?
- What size will their sheet of wallpaper be? Explain that it should not be too big for them to handle: about 50 square cm is a good size. Let them cut a piece of paper to the size they want.
- Encourage the children to evaluate their designs as they proceed. They should stand well back from their work and view it from a distance, as well as having the opportunity to discuss and comment on each other's work.

- When the sheets of wallpaper are made, the children can decide which glue they want to use, and make up enough to cover their sheet of wallpaper. They can then all paste their wallpaper to the sheet of hardboard/cardboard.

EVALUATION
- Are the children pleased with their wallpaper design? Would they like it in their room? Are there any changes they would make? What do they think of each other's designs?

- Did the glue stick? Did the children's wallpaper stay up?

EXTENSION ACTIVITIES
- Test a variety of different commercial glues. What sort of materials do they stick? Are some stronger than others?
  WARNING: This is an opportunity to warn about the dangers of sniffing glues.

- Test different adhesive tapes as an alternative to glue/paste. What materials do they stick together? Can you paint over all the tapes? Why not? Which tapes can you paint over? Experiment by painting over different types of tapes. What did you find out?

- Make resource boards to display the information for future designing and making reference.

LANGUAGE OPPORTUNITIES
- Emphasise that writing can be used for different effects in display, considering features of layout and presentation, and refining work to make it clear and easily read.

- Ask the children to choose a name for their wallpaper design and to write an advertisement listing its various qualities. Develop the use of persuasive language to promote their wallpaper design.

Teacher's notes:
If you do use commercial wallpaper paste, make sure that you obtain one with no anti-fungal chemicals in it, as these are poisonous.

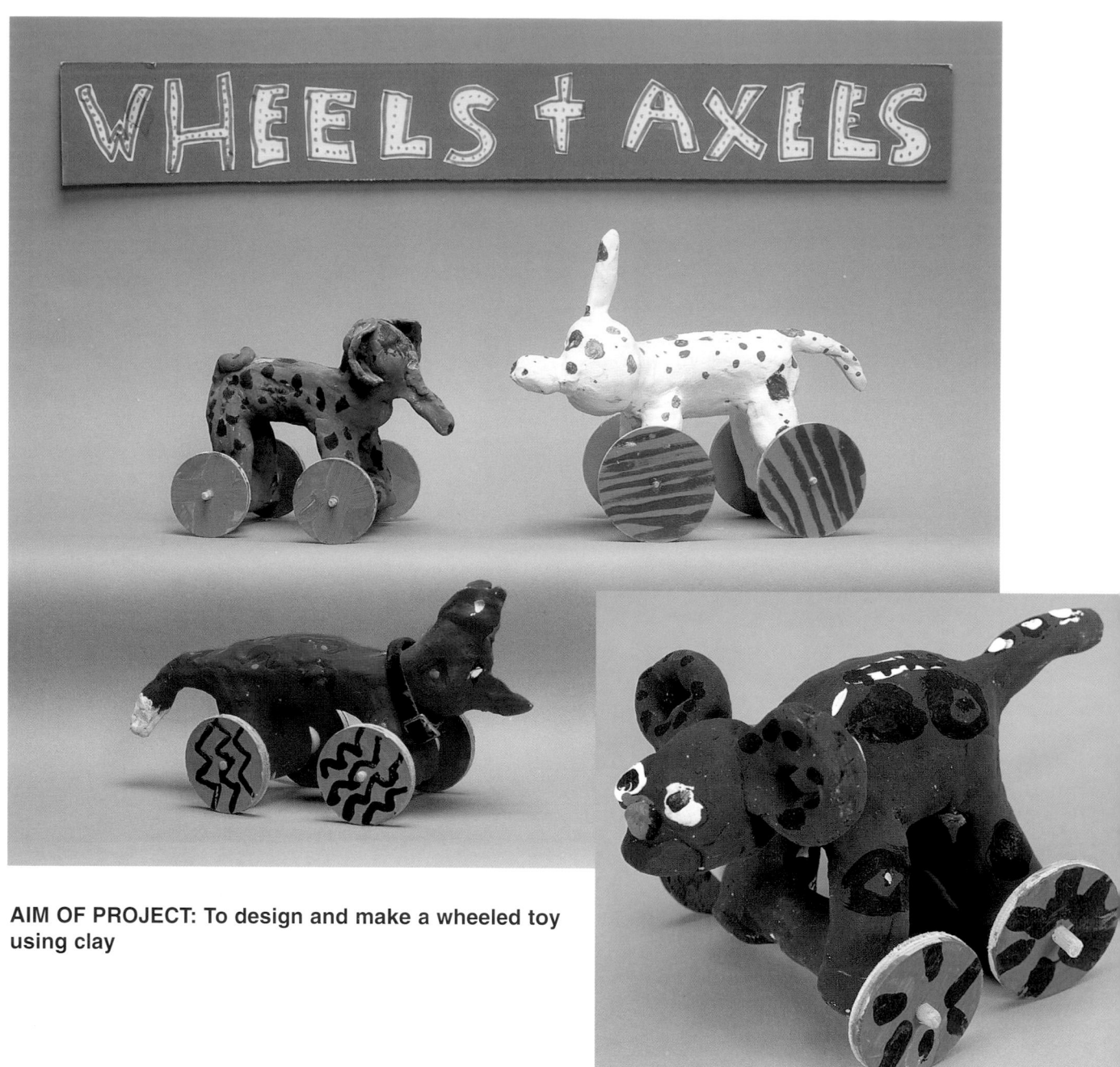

AIM OF PROJECT: To design and make a wheeled toy using clay

RESOURCES

Small boxes, dowel, hole punches
Straws, strong card triangles
Saws and vices for cutting dowel
Card discs with holes in the centre (for wheels)
Soft, malleable air-drying clay
Paint and brushes
Construction bricks

STARTING POINTS

• Ask the children to bring in examples of small wheeled toys. Let them examine them carefully. Discuss how these toys have been made. Why do the wheels turn? Are they *push* toys? or *pull* toys? Which do you like best? Why?

• Discuss how toys are designed. Talk about designers having to consider what other people like and how to design attractive products. Ask them to think about designing a toy that they would like to buy in a shop.

INVESTIGATIONS

- Test some of the toys. How far/fast do the children's toys move when you push them? when you pull them? Devise a fair test to find out.

- Let the children try pushing a small box filled with weights. Does it move easily? Why not?

- Try putting a row of pencils underneath the box. Push again. Does the box move more easily? Why? Introduce the word *friction* and discuss the children's understanding of this. Explain that friction is a force that opposes motion.

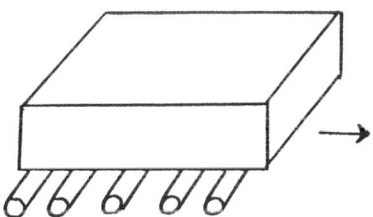

- Have available a selection of small boxes, short lengths of dowelling, and card discs for wheels, for the children to make wheel and axle vehicles to experiment with.

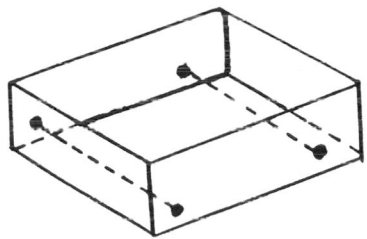

Make holes in a box with a hole puncher.

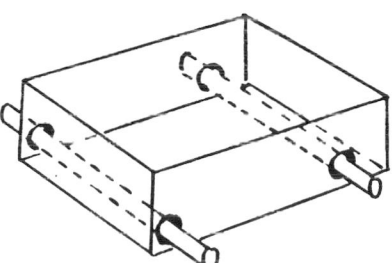

Push dowel through the holes.

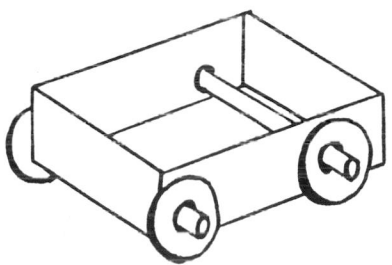

Push card discs onto dowel.

- The easiest method of making a wheel and axle, is to fix the wheels tightly to the axles, allowing the axles to run freely in the holes of the chassis.

- Show them how to punch holes in the side of their boxes and push the dowel through, and then push card dics onto the dowel. What happens if the wheels do not fit on to the axle tightly? Does the vehicle move? Why not? How can you make the wheels fit tightly? Show the children how to tape or glue the wheels to the axles. Do the wheels now turn when the axle turns? Does your model move?

- Explain that the axles need to be aligned for the wheels to run straight.

- Let the children try making a box where the axles are not aligned, and observe what happens. Do the wheels move in a straight line? How do they move? Can they work out why?

Aligned	**Not aligned**

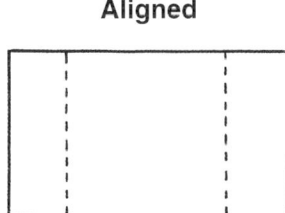

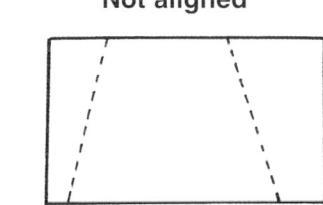

- Are the card discs strong enough? How can they be made stronger? Show the children how to glue the discs together. How strong are three card discs glued together?

65

- The children can make a display board of all their findings.

- The children can experiment with other ways of making wheels and axles with the axle moving freely in the chassis.

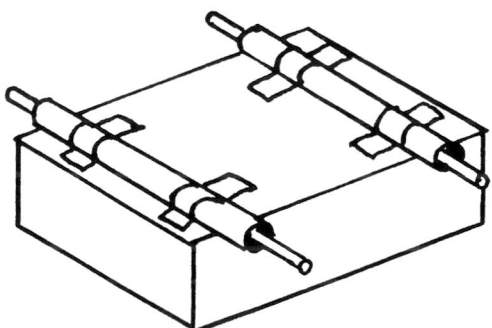

Straws taped to box, dowel pushed through straws and card discs pushed on to dowel.

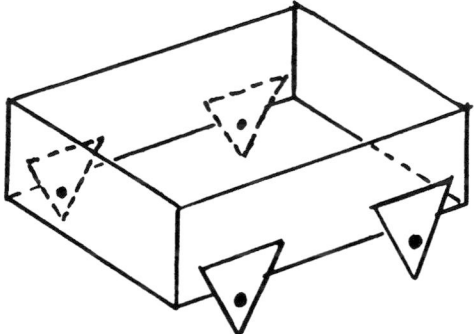

Strong card triangles with holes punched into them, glued to box. Dowels pushed through holes and card discs pushed onto dowels.

- Once the children are satisfied with their vehicles, they can use them to investigate the distances they will travel after going down a ramp supported by one construction brick. Encourage them to consider how to make their tests fair.

- Can they predict and write down the distance their models will travel with a ramp supported by two construction bricks? three bricks? four bricks? etc.

- Let them write down their predictions and then test their model for height of ramp and distance travelled.

- Encourage them to observe and record their results using bar charts.

- Encourage the children to experiment further. Does the distance change if you push your vehicle from the top of the ramp, instead of just letting it roll?

- How can you change the direction of your vehicle?

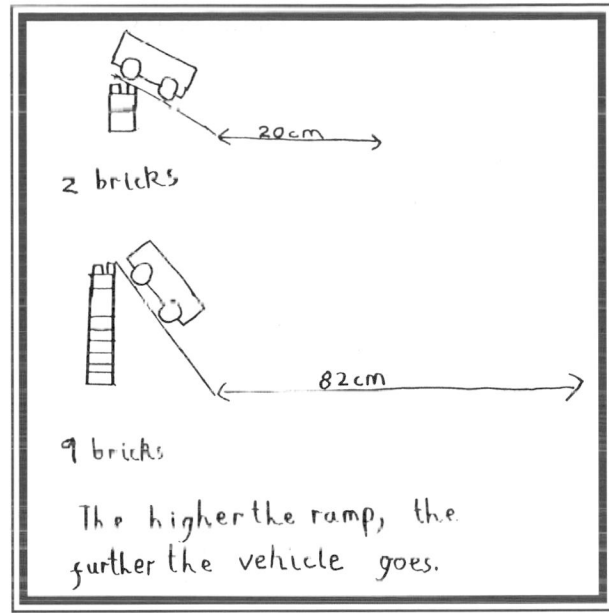

2 bricks

82 cm

9 bricks

The higher the ramp, the further the vehicle goes.

- The children can also try their wheel and axle models on different surfaces as they come off the ramp, such as tarmac, sandpaper, sand, polished floor, etc. Do their models move at different speeds on different surfaces? On which surface do they move faster? On which surfaces do they move more slowly? Why do they move at different speeds? Explore how friction acts against the direction of motion, causing objects to slow down and stop.

ASSIGNMENTS
To design and make a wheeled toy

Designing
- Let the children look at photographs or books with information on wheeled toys, or look at toys from the class collection. How are the wheels attached to the toy? Where are the axles? How do you think that it moves? Do you think that it is a *push* or a *pull* toy?

NOTE: For this project, we used photographs of an Aztec toy and the children decorated their toys using Aztec patterns as inspiration. This type of toy was made about 500 years ago by an Aztec craftsman in Mexico. (The example shown in the photograph above is a modern reproduction.)

- Encourage the children to sketch their ideas, considering carefully where their axles will be placed. Let them also think about colours and decorations for their toys.

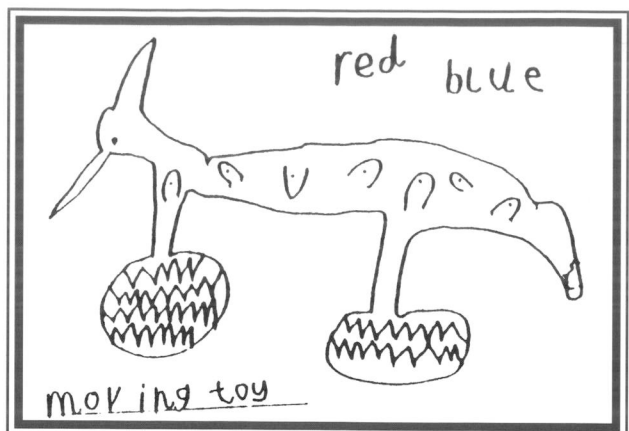

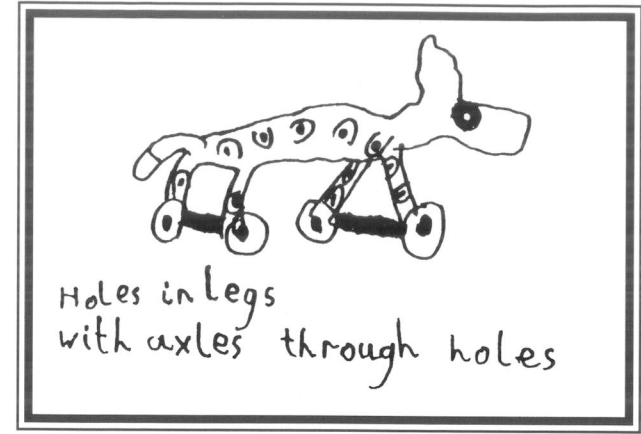

Making

- Let the children feel the clay. Encourage them to use words to describe what forces they are exerting: for example, *squashing, pushing, pulling, stretching,* etc.

- Give them objects to press into the clay to make impressed patterns and to create texture.

- As they start making their toys, explain that they will need 'clay glue' (see Techniques, page 6) for every join. Remind them that the clay needs to dry before it can be painted.

- Explain that they will need to put in axle holes while the clay is still wet. Remind them to align the axles. Where will they be? Is their toy sturdy enough to hold the axle? Do the legs need to be joined together for strength like the Aztec toy in the photograph (on the previous page)? How will they make the holes? They can push a pencil through the clay, as this will leave a large enough diameter (allowing for shrinkage of the clay whilst drying) in which the dowel can move freely.

- The children can weigh their toy while it is still wet. Once their toy has dried, let them weigh it again and consider the new weight of their toy. Why is there a difference?

- Consider the strength of the card wheels. Remind them that they can make the discs stronger by gluing them together. How many layers do they think that the wheels on their toy will need? Let them feel the ones they made for their display board to help them decide.

- The children can measure and cut their dowel using saws and vices (see Introduction). They should then fit their axles and glue their wheels onto the dowel. They might find that the wheels rub on the toys, and so do not move freely. This is an opportunity to discuss how friction affects movement. Show them how to put spacers (short lengths of straw or a small sponge disc) between their vehicle and the wheel.

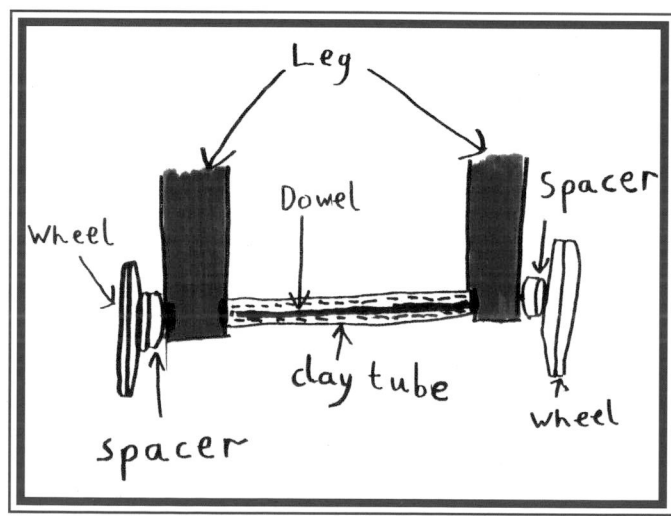

- Decorate the toy according to their original design. Remind the children that it is best to paint the whole toy in one colour, and once this is dry, apply the patterns.

EVALUATION

• Does your toy move well? Does it look good? How could you improve it? Would you buy it in a shop?

• Show your toys to another class. What do they think of them?

EXTENSION ACTIVITIES

• The children can investigate making wheels of different shapes. How well do these move?

• What happens if they place the holes for the axles off-centre? How does this change the way their vehicle moves?

Box design for a wheeled toy.

LANGUAGE OPPORTUNITIES

- Collect toy boxes and ask the children to consider why boxes are needed for toys. Encourage the children to read logos, advertisements and writing on the boxes. What is the purpose of the writing, etc.? Consider the way that the boxes themselves are an extension of the advertising. What sort of persuasive language has been used on the box?

- Design and make a box for your wheeled toy using the measurements of the toy. Do they need to be decorated? Why? Will your box have a logo? What will you call your toy? What will you write on your box? Will your box have a bar code?

- Encourage the children to take photographs of their toy (or someone playing with it) to decorate the box.

Teacher's notes:

- A wheel and axle consist of two different sized cylinders fitted into one another. Because the diameter of the wheel is bigger than the diameter of the axle, one 360° turn of the axle produces a bigger turn of the wheel.

- Pushes and pulls are examples of forces. Forces can make things speed up, slow down or change direction.

NOTES

For details of further Belair publications,
please write to: Libby Masters,
BELAIR PUBLICATIONS LIMITED,
Albert House, Apex Business Centre,
Boscombe Road, Dunstable, LU5 4RL.

For sales and distribution in North America and South America,
INCENTIVE PUBLICATIONS,
3835 Cleghorn Avenue, Nashville, Tn 37215.
USA.

For sales and distribution in Australia
EDUCATIONAL SUPPLIES PTY LTD
8 Cross Street, Brookvale, NSW 2100.
Australia

For sales and distribution (in other territories)
FOLENS PUBLISHERS
Albert House, Apex Business Centre,
Boscombe Road, Dunstable, LU5 4RL.
United Kingdom.
E-mail: folens@folens.com